INTRODUCTION TO TECHNICAL CERAMICS

INTRODUCTION TO
TECHNICAL CERAMICS

by
B. E. WAYE
M.Sc., F.R.I.C., A.R.C.S., F.I.Ceram.

MACLAREN AND SONS LTD.
LONDON

Made and printed in England by
LIVESEY LTD., ST. JOHN'S HILL, SHREWSBURY.

LIST OF CONTENTS

FOREWORD

Whilst there is an extensive literature on the newer types of ceramic materials which have been developed in recent years, there has been a need for some time for a book where this material is collected in a form suitable for students and others whose work brings them into contact with these developments.

Mr. Waye, who has had industrial experience in this field and also considerable teaching experience at the College of Ceramics in Stoke-on-Trent where he is a Principal Lecturer, has now produced such a book. The emphasis is on technological rather than scientific aspects and it will provide a sound introduction to those who may wish to pursue the subject in more detail by using the references which he has given at the end of the sections. I hope this book will have the success it deserves.

W. L. GERMAN, D.Sc., Ph.D., F.R.I.C., F.I. Ceram.
College of Ceramics,
Stoke - on - Trent.

PREFACE

Over 20 years have elapsed since the publication of E. Rosenthal's "Porcelain and Other Ceramic Insulating Materials" in 1944, and there has been for some time a demand, particularly by students, for a book devoted specifically to technical ceramics, with the coverage extended to include the more important non-traditional ceramics developed since that time.

The present volume is based largely on a lecture course at the College of Ceramics and is aimed to provide an introductory survey. Readers having a sound, even if rather elementary, scientific background should experience no great difficulty in the text, but those who are unfamiliar with conventional ceramics would benefit by first reading a book such as "Modern Ceramic Practice" by the late A. J. Dale, and by consulting the "Dictionary of Ceramics" by A. E. Dodd. The series of Institute of Ceramics textbooks would also make useful supplementary reading.

The first eight chapters of the present book cover mainly the more conventional technical ceramics and methods of manufacture ; the remaining seven deal with the newer types and their technology. As most students of ceramics are less familiar with electrical and magnetic properties than with others, appendices have been included, giving relevant definitions and information on methods of testing.

Much of the material in the book first appeared in a series of articles published in *Ceramics*, and the author is grateful to Arrow Press Ltd. for permission to reproduce it here.

The author acknowledges useful comments made by colleagues at the College of Ceramics and by members of the staff of the British Ceramic Research Association. Particular thanks are due to Dr. J. A. Sugden and to Mr. P. Popper, who kindly made detailed comments on the manuscript.

B. E. WAYE

August, 1966   *Stoke-on-Trent.*

CHAPTER 1

INTRODUCTION

1.1 Terminology

The term "technical ceramics" might be assumed, in its widest sense, to cover all non-consumer products, that is all ceramics that are not in themselves end products, such as tableware, but form components of some other product. On this basis, however, it would be necessary to include structural ceramics, refractories, etc., which are distinct branches of the industry ; these must therefore be excluded from our definition. Naturally there must be occasional overlapping, as in the cases of oxide refractories, glass-ceramics and cermets. Having noted the exclusions from the definition, we are left with a minor, but important section of the ceramic industry, which is expanding rapidly, not only in volume, but more strikingly in the variety of new materials, techniques and applications made possible by intensive development along quite novel lines.

Electroceramics form by far the largest group of products, being followed by chemical ware and by numerous components for mechanical and nuclear applications, as well as for space flight. An alternative term might have been "engineering ceramics", but even here there would have been obvious exceptions. The term "special ceramics" is normally applied to a more restricted field, and in any case is not easy to define precisely. Were it not for the inclusion of traditional electrical and chemical porcelain (chemical stoneware is excluded from this book), our field of interest might well have been defined as "non-clay ceramics", since clay forms either a minor constituent of most of the newer technical ceramics, or else is completely absent.

1.2 Economic importance

The annual value of electrical porcelain produced in this country runs at about £11 million, that is about 7 % of the total of all ceramic products. Figures for other types of electrical and special ceramics are not readily available, but it is worth noting that in at least one of the larger, old established domestic ware companies, over half the

1

turnover is now accounted for by technical ceramics. A number of the larger engineering firms and government agencies are developing and manufacturing their own special ceramics, and the sparking plug manufacturers are increasingly undertaking the manufacture of various special alumina products. There are also half a dozen or so large electrical and chemical porcelain manufacturers and many medium and small firms who concentrate on highly specialised products like capacitors, piezoelectric and magnetic ceramics.

To appreciate the developments that have taken place one has only to look back to the period of the First World War. Electrical porcelain was then used mainly for low tension, direct current ; or for low frequency alternating current, in telegraphy, electric lighting and a few power applications. For such purposes there were no very stringent specifications, and the ordinary "pot" insulators were adequate. By 1930 high tension electric transmission was well established, and radiocommunication, using very much higher frequencies, was getting into its stride. The former demanded porcelain of much higher quality, and the latter the development of new compositions. Today electroceramics embraces a great variety of highly specialised components for the electrical and above all for the electronics industry ; these range in size from miniature parts of overall dimensions of only a few thousandths of an inch with unique electrical or magnetic properties, to high tension porcelain bushings over 10 ft. in height, capable of carrying conductors at up to half-a-million volts, and resisting the most adverse weather conditions.

Although porcelain accounts for the bulk of the products, the relative importance of the newer materials is increasing steadily, in particular alumina products. Industry is now appreciating that ceramics can in many cases be "tailor-made" to fulfill functions that would have been unthinkable only a few years ago. There are many problems in engineering today that neither plastics, metals, nor conventional ceramics are adequate to solve. These present a challenge which is being met by completely new approaches based upon fundamental studies of materials. Table 1.1 lists a selection from the more important uses of technical ceramics. One could continue to quote other examples of new types and applications, such as numerous semi-conducting devices like rectifiers and transistors ;

TABLE 1.1

Important uses of technical ceramics

Applications	Types of Ceramics
Electrical	
Low and high tension insulation	
Domestic fittings, power generation and transmission.	Electrical porcelain, zircon porcelain
Insulation at elevated temperatures	
Insulation for electric fires, ovens and low temperature kilns	Aluminous porcelain, cordierite
Insulation for fire-proof cables	Magnesia
Insulation at high temperatures	
Thermocouple sheaths, furnace muffles, various furnace parts	Mullite, fused silica, alumina
Sparking plug insulators	Alumina
Electronic	
High frequency insulation	
Rods, tubes, plates, coil formers, valve parts.	Steatite, zircon porcelain, alumina
Capacitor dielectrics	
Trimmer capacitors	Steatite
High permittivity dielectrics	Rutile, titanates
Transmitter capacitor dielectrics	Rutile, magnesium titanate
"Non-linear" dielectrics	
Dielectric amplifiers, memory units, accelerometers, electromechanical transducers (e.g. gramophone pick-up crystals, ultrasonic generators)	Barium titanate, lead zirconate-titanate
Semi-conductors	
Non-linear resistors, e.g. thermistors	Silicon, silicon carbide, germanium
Rectifiers, transistors	
Magnetic components	
Inductor and transformer cores	Manganese-zinc and nickel-zinc ferrites
Cores for memory devices	Manganese-magnesium ferrite
Microwave components	Nickel ferrite and manganese-aluminium ferrite
Permanent magnets	Barium ferrite
Nuclear	
Fuel elements	Uranium and plutonium oxides, carbides and nitrides
Moderators	Beryllium oxide, graphite
Control and shut-down rods	Boron carbide

3

TABLE 1.1 (*continued*)

Applications	Types of Ceramics
Chemical and Metallurgical	
Laboratory ware	"Hard" porcelain, zircon porcelain, alumina
Reaction vessels	Fused silica, porcelain, alumina
Catalyst supports	Alumina
Special metallurgical operations	Refractory oxides, carbides, etc., calcium fluoride
Mechanical and Thermal	
At normal temperatures	
Abrasive grinding wheels	Alumina, silicon carbide, with ceramic glassy bond ; fused alumina
Cutting tools	Alumina, carbides
Dies for wire drawing	Alumina
Textile guides	Alumina, rutile
Pump parts	Alumina
Grinding mills and media	Porcelain, alumina
At high temperatures	
High temperature lubrication	Graphite, boron nitride
Rocket nozzles, nose cones, etc.	Various refractory oxides and non-oxides
Friction materials	Cermets

infra-red sensitive cadmium sulphide used to control the centreless grinding of roller bearings to an accuracy of a few microns ; ceramic fibres, paper and cloth ; vitreous enamels containing electroluminescent zinc sulphide, which convert electricity directly into light and single crystal devices like lasers. Only a few of these can, however, be dealt with in this book.

1.3 Properties

Naturally these new developments have demanded not only radical improvements in the more usual properties of ceramics but a range of special properties and combinations of properties. Technical ceramics are usually made to closer dimensional tolerances than other types of ware, mainly because of the need to match other components, sometimes with very high accuracy. Many products have to have the highest tensile or compressive strength obtainable. The rigidity of ceramics in general and their resistance to abrasion and to chemical attack gives them an advantage over most metals, particularly at high operating temperatures, and these characteristics have been exploited to a high degree in technical ceramics. On the other hand, the notorious brittleness of ceramics, whilst annoying in the domestic field, is far more serious in circumstances in which failure of one ceramic component means failure of a complete piece of complex equipment. Much attention has been paid to this problem, but there appears to have been no significant progress towards a solution.

A little more success has resulted from an intensive study of a related problem—comparatively poor resistance to thermal stress and thermal shock, but it would seem that composite products of ceramics with metals or other materials offer the best prospect of overcoming these two problems.

A property that is usually much more important in technical ceramics than in other types is porosity, and with few exceptions apparent porosity must not exceed 0.1 % ; in fact for many purposes the aim is zero *total* porosity, with the bulk density approaching as nearly as possible the true or theoretical density, in order to obtain optimum mechanical, electrical or other properties. Very careful control of the microstructure of many technical ceramics is necessary; the type, size, quantity and distribution of the phases present are all important. Microstructure and texture are both important. The latter term is not easy to define, but may be taken to mean the degree of long-range uniformity (either bulk or surface). The presence of inhomogeneities such as large pores or large areas of different phases could seriously affect mechanical, electrical or other properties, as indeed could other departures from optimum structure. Apart from the fairly obvious electrical requirement of high resistivity for insulators, numerous other electrical and magnetic properties, some of them quite complex, are required for particular applications. Finally, chemical stability in a variety of situations is required, particularly in the metallurgy of some of the newer metals, and in nuclear reactors.

CHAPTER 2

RAW MATERIALS

2.1 General

Raw materials may be either naturally occurring ones as used in the more traditional ceramics, such as : clays, freed from gross impurities by physical methods such as elutriation ; substances extracted from minerals and chemically purified, e.g. alumina, obtained from bauxite ; or purely synthetic materials like barium titanate and the ferrites, as well as organic additives used as aids to shaping. Many of the newer ceramics demand high purity, and amounts of even less than 1% of certain impurities (naturally occurring or deliberately added) can have a marked influence on microstructure and final properties, e.g. magnesium oxide added to alumina (see under 9.4.6). In some semiconducting ceramics the level of impurity has to be as low as about 1 in 10^{-8} ; in fact such products are really fine chemicals. Even with the more common materials contamination should be avoided at all stages of production.

Close control of grain size and, in some materials, shape, are at least as important as chemical purity, since not only do they affect shaping and vitrification, but also the degree of reaction between solids during the calcination process used to synthesise certain compounds.

No attempt will be made here to deal with anything more than a selection of raw materials of fairly general interest ; others will be dealt with when considering particular products. Readers requiring further information are referred to the comprehensive list published annually in *Ceramic Industry*.

2.2 Clays

Since clays form something like half of the recipe of electrical porcelain, they account for the largest consumption of raw materials. Little needs to be said here on the sources and properties of clays, as the subject is already covered in the literature dealing with other branches of the industry. One or two points should be mentioned however. Although, as in pottery, mixtures of ball clays and china

6

clay are used, the function of the latter in giving a white colour is less important in technical porcelain than in domestic ware. The choice is dictated by their effect on drying and firing shrinkage—particularly important in attaining close dimensional tolerances, and on firing characteristics like fluxing, rigidity and vitrification. China clays selected particularly for porcelain are now marketed, with a low mica content, e.g. 12% (analysis calculated on the mica convention).

The usual control tests on clays are employed : drying and firing shrinkage ; dry and fired strength (sometimes a 50:50 clay : quartz mixture is used) ; vitrification ; and less frequently, chemical analysis and grain size determination. Occasionally the base exchange values of clays are determined on a routine basis when slip casting is to be used. Plasticity is of course an important if ill-defined property, and clays of high plasticity are required in compounding otherwise comparatively non-plastic bodies. Too low plasticity may give cracking during severe working of the clays, and low dry strength, resulting in high handling losses. Generally the finer the clay the greater its plasticity, and in cases where only a small proportion of clay is permissible in a body, bentonite may be added, either alone or with a small amount of ball clay ; discretion has to be used, however, as the fine material may cause undue slowing down of filterpressing and high drying shrinkage.

Bentonite, which is derived from volcanic ash, belongs to the *montmorillonite* group of clays ; the formula can be derived from *pyrophyllite*, $Al_2Si_4O_{10}(OH)_2$, by replacement of one-third of one of the Al's by Na or Mg, and it can be written $Al_{1.67}(Mg/Na)_{0.33}Si_4O_{10}(OH)_2$. It differs from *kaolinite*, $Al_2Si_2O_5(OH)_4$, in having a symmetrical sheet of an Al-OH octahedral layer sandwiched between two tetrahedral Si-O sheets, instead of consisting of alternate sheets. Replacement of one of the (trivalent) Al's by (divalent) Mg gives a net negative charge to the unit cell, which has to be balanced by adsorbed ions. Montmorillonite minerals are unique in that water molecules can enter between the sheets of oxygens lying on both sides of the "sandwich", and cause swelling ; this is because of the much weaker bonding (van der Waals forces) between the unit cells compared to that in the case of kaolin, which has hydroxyls on one side of the cell. Swelling, as well as the extremely small particle size of bentonite (substantially less than 0.5 micron, i.e. some 20 times less than that of ball clays) makes it a very effective plasticiser. Being inorganic, it leaves a residue on firing, which may be objectionable, and its quality is variable, both as regards impurities like soda and iron compounds, as well as in its effectiveness as a plasticiser. Tests have been devised for the latter property, consisting of comparing the degree of gel formation when mixed with water. Care has to be taken in blending in mixes because of its tendency to become sticky and to form clots when wet, causing uneven mixing. One method is to dry mix with some of the other constituents before wetting.

Other clays are used, according to local availability, on the Continent and elsewhere ; naturally efforts are made to use indigenous clays and other raw materials, particularly in the newly developing countries.

A clay product used for some types of ware, such as electric heating element insulators, is known by its trade name "Molochite" and is a calcined grog prepared from kaolin. It is obtainable in various grades of fineness, ranging from the quite coarse material as used in refractories, to a very fine flour. Conversion to the refractory compound mullite is claimed to be 96% of the maximum possible, and this assists in conferring thermal shock resistance.

2.3 Silica

Silica is normally used in one of the forms of quartz, e.g. sand, crushed rock, or quartzite, since the advantages of using flint in earthenware do not apply to vitreous bodies such as porcelain ; some manufacturers do, however, use flint. In either case the grain size is very important, and affects the working properties of the body. If sand is used it must be white sand, free from iron ; sources in this country include Loch Aline and Aylesbury. Most manufacturers buy it already ground to a specified fineness, for example 50-55% less than 0.01 mm. For routine control fineness is most conveniently determined by the sedimentation (hydrometer) method.

2.4 Fluxes

Cornish stone, familiar to pottery manufacturers, is variable in composition, and is not such an effective flux as *felspar*, which is therefore normally preferred. Scandinavian felspar is the type mostly used in this country. Although grain size is perhaps not quite so important as in the case of quartz, it must be controlled, the usual range of fineness being similar to that of quartz. It is also important to control its chemical composition, since variations in alkali content, and also in the potash/soda ratio may have important effects on firing behaviour and fired properties. Not only do potash and soda felspars melt at different temperatures, but they also form eutectics of different melting points with other body constituents such as silica and metakaolin. The natural felspars are mainly potash felspar (orthoclase), with some soda felspar (albite), and small amounts of calcium felspar (anorthite).

Commercial high potash felspars melt in the range 1100 to 1200°C. Pure potash felspar melts incongruently at about 1150°C. yielding crystals of leucite and a silica-rich liquid, melting being complete at 1530°C :

$$KAlSi_3O_8 \longrightarrow KAlSi_2O_6 + SiO_2$$

A fusion ("button") test is a useful method for routine control : a sample of each batch is fired, together with a standard sample, in a small depression in a refractory plate, and the fusibility and colour are compared.

Occasionally felspar sand is used as a source of felspar. On the Continent *pegmatites* (somewhat similar to Cornish stone) are used as the flux in porcelain.

Nepheline syenite, $NaAlSiO_4$, has been used for some time in the United States, and a high quality material from the North Cape in Norway is now marketed in this country.

2.5 Aluminous materials

Sillimanite and *kyanite* are useful sources of alumina for use in refractory insulators. These minerals, which occur in large deposits in India, have the theoretical composition Al_2SiO_5. On heating, the refractory compound *mullite*, $Al_6Si_2O_{13}$ or $3Al_2O_3 2SiO_2$, and silica are formed. Synthetic mullite has already been mentioned, and is formed during the firing of bodies containing clay or felspar or both. Sintered synthetic mullite, made from low-iron bauxite, is an active competitor of the material made from naturally occurring minerals ; it is made in a state of high purity in the electric furnace by the fusion of pure alumina and siliceous materials.

Alumina itself is produced chiefly from *bauxite*, $Al_2O_3.2H_2O$, found in Jamaica, British Guiana, Europe and elsewhere. Purification from associated oxides, mainly silica and iron oxide, is by the Baeyer process, which consists in dissolving the bauxite in caustic soda, and precipitating aluminium hydroxide, $Al(OH)_3$, from the solution, by passing carbon dioxide through. The hydroxide is washed, dried, and finally calcined. Because of the use of soda in this process, the final product still contains 0.1—0.2% of Na_2O, apart from other residual impurities like SiO_2, Fe_2O_3, CaO, TiO_2 and Cr_2O_3, with occasionally traces of vanadium. The presence of Na_2O and to a less extent SiO_2 is apt to be troublesome if highly refractory high alumina products are to be made, and purer materials can be obtained if necessary.

Both the hydrates and the oxide are commercially available. The former, on heating to about 500°C., yield alumina in a very active form, γ-*alumina*. This has a defect spinel structure and consists of extremely fine crystals, which accounts for its reactivity. It has been used as an addition to high alumina bodies to promote sintering. On heating to about 1000°C. this and all other metastable forms of alumina are converted into the stable form, α-*alumina* or *corundum*, the grain size increasing with increasing calcination temperature. If alumina hydrate is milled to a specified grain size before calcining, the grain size of the calcined material can be controlled within close limits, only a short final milling being necessary to break up aggregates. Ground *fused* alumina has occasionally been used, but *calcined* alumina is the material normally used, at a grain size of around 2 microns. It is now available in specially graded form, with a fairly wide spread in grain sizes, in order to give close packing ; a pressed density of about 75% of theoretical can be obtained, enabling high fired densities to be obtained with quite low shrinkages.

Another comparatively recent commercial form of alumina is *tabular alumina*, which consists substantially of large crystals of α-alumina, formed by sintering at temperatures near the melting point (2040°C.). The advantages are that the purity is improved by the volatilisation of most of the residual soda ; and that internal pores are largely eliminated from the crystals, which therefore have a high apparent density, low and consistent shrinkage, giving high density in the product. However, tabular alumina is difficult to grind because of its hardness, and is more suitable for applications such as castable refractories.

2.6 Magnesian materials

Both *magnesium oxide* and *magnesium carbonate* are used as ingredients in numerous bodies. The oxide, MgO, is produced mainly from natural or from sea-water magnesite by calcination. *Caustic calcined* magnesia is made by calcining natural magnesite at a temperature somewhat below 1560°C., and retains from 2 to 10% of CO_2. *Dead burnt* magnesium oxide is made by calcining to a higher temperature ; it should contain very little CO_2 and show no tendency to re-hydrate. A rough check is to add a small amount of water and to observe whether a thermometer placed in the mixture shows any rise in temperature. For accuracy in body mixing, the MgO content should be known. Chemically purified material is, of course, necessary for making pure magnesium oxide ceramics.

Talc, another source of MgO, and commonly used in other branches of the industry, is an important constituent of cordierite and steatite ceramics. *Steatite* is properly the massive form of talc, but the term has come to be used also for ceramics made mainly from talc. Talc was formed by the hydration of magnesium-bearing rocks under pressure, and occurs in various parts of the world ; the main sources for use in this country are Egypt and India. It is the softest known mineral (No. 1 on Mohs' scale), is easily shaped when in block form, but is not plastic. Porous insulators have been made for many years by machining block talc to size, and firing ; steatite bodies with talc as an ingredient came much later.

Natural talc contains a number of impurities, but ideally is a hydrated magnesium silicate, $Mg_3Si_4O_{10}(OH)_2$. It has a layer structure analagous to pyrophyllite, only with a layer of *brucite*, $Mg(OH)_2$, sandwiched between the silica layers. This explains its softness and ease of cleavage. Montmorillonite can equally well be regarded as structurally derived from talc as from pyrophyllite.

The percentages of MgO and SiO_2 in a good quality talc are about 51—53, and about 57—62 respectively, and the ignition loss is up to 5%. Small amounts of Al_2O_3, CaO, Fe_2O_3 and TiO_2 may also be present, and these must be known, as they may affect the vitrification, final microstructure and electrical properties of low-loss steatite ceramics. An ignition test is useful as a control ; it

11

shows up any specking due to large particles of impurities, and colour changes may indicate changes in iron content.

Particle size and shape are also important, because if very large platelets are present, difficulty may be experienced due to a tendency to laminate during extrusion, and to a less extent during pressing. For this reason some manufacturers calcine and mill the more platey talc before use ; alternatively dry milling or comminution, for example through a swinging hammer mill, may be used. Talc is difficult to wet-mill, as it is not readily wetted, and tends to aggregate.

The particle size and shape of natural talcs vary considerably ; Egyptian and Indian materials tend to be less platey (more granular) than Australian and Chinese.

2.7 Alkaline earths

Calcium, strontium and barium carbonates are used for various purposes, e.g. as non-alkaline fluxes, and to make important classes of compounds : titanates and ferrites. Calcium and barium carbonates are also used in glazes. The pure precipitated carbonates are readily available, and chemical analysis is normally unneccesary, but grain size is sometimes important because of its effect on rates of solid state reactions.

2.8 Lead compounds

These are used to a limited extent in lead glazes, although leadless, felspathic glazes are much commoner. The pure oxides and the carbonate are used in making titanates, zirconates, etc.

2.9 Titanium oxide

The *dioxide*, TiO_2, exists in three crystalline forms : *brookite*, *anatase* and *rutile*, all of which have abnormally high dielectric constants, rutile having the highest and being of the most interest because of its use in high permittivity dielectrics. The source of titanium oxide is the mineral *ilmenite*, which is mainly ferrous titanate, and is found in Norway, Travancore and elsewhere. It is converted into TiO_2 in the anatase modification by chemical precipitation from a purified solution of titanium tetrachloride. Anatase is sometimes used directly in rutile bodies, since it is in any case converted to rutile on firing. However, it is an advantage to convert anatase to rutile first, by pre-calcining at about 1000°C., as this increases the density from 3.8 g/cc. to 4.2 g/cc. thus giving less firing shrinkage ; the calcination also helps to lower the drying shrinkage of the body by growing the otherwise extremely fine grains and by altering their size distribution so as to give closer packing. Some impurities, for example iron oxide, could have an adverse effect on the electrical properties of both rutile and titanate products, and must be avoided.

2.10 Zirconium compounds

Zircon, $ZrSiO_4$, occurs in alluvial sands in Ceylon, Madagascar and Australia. It is commercially available in chemically purified form, ground to varying degrees of fineness. Its melting point is 2420°C., its thermal conductivity is good, it has a low coefficient of thermal expansion ($4 \times 10^{-6}/°C$. between 20 and 1000°C.) and is resistant to thermal stress and to chemical attack. Its main uses are as a refractory in the glass industry and in metallurgy, and as a moulding sand ; it is also a useful refractory for kiln furniture. It is commonly used as a glaze opacifier on account of its low solubility in glazes and its high refractive index. In electroceramics it is the major constituent of zircon porcelain.

Zirconia, ZrO_2, is extracted from zircon and from the mineral *baddeleyite*, which occurs in Brazil and contains 80—90% of ZrO_2. It is a constituent of a number of electrical and special ceramics. Its properties and uses are discussed later. Zirconia contains varying amounts of *hafnium oxide*, HfO_2, as impurity ; this is of interest in ceramics for nuclear energy.

2.11 Manganese compounds

These are used in special glazes and in ferrites. Several grades and types of compound are available, ranging from high grade ores to highly purified synthetic compounds. The commonest form employed is finely ground *pyrolusite*, which consists mainly of the dioxide, MnO_2. When purer material is necessary the precipitated *carbonate* or *hydrated oxide* is used.

2.12 Iron compounds

Synthetic iron oxide, which is produced mainly as a paint pigment, and also to a minor extent for ceramic colours, is used, along with other oxides, for making brown and semi-conducting glazes for high tension insulators, and is the major constituent of ferrites. It is made either by chemical methods starting with metallic iron, or by roasting the ore *copperas*, $FeSO_4.7H_2O$. The shape and size of the particles, their colour and reactivity, depend on the processing details. Grain size is very important, particularly in the manufacture of ferrites, since here again, the degree of reaction in the solid state with the other constituents has a great influence on final properties.

2.13 Other inorganic materials

Many other oxides, e.g. *zinc* and *nickel oxides*—used in ferrites— and *uranium, thorium* and *hafnium oxides*—used in nuclear reactors— should be noted. *Carbon*, normally in the form of *graphite*, is frequently shaped by ceramic methods, although its inclusion as a ceramic material may be questioned, and is used for the same types of application as ceramics, e.g. in nuclear reactors, muffles, crucibles. These materials will be discussed in the sections dealing with their particular technologies.

2.14 Organic additives[1]

With the coming into use of materials of low plasticity, like the pure refractory oxides, shaping methods such as extrusion and pressing, which depend on the plasticity and dry strength of clays, could only be used by the aid of suitable substitutes to give the necessary plasticity and strength. In addition to *plasticisers* and *bonds, lubricants* were required in shaping abrasive ceramics like alumina. The use of bentonite has already been mentioned (2.2), but there are many modern ceramic products in which any residue is detrimental, and therefore organic compounds, of which a large selection is now available, have to be employed.

Plasticisers and bonds are colloids forming either sols or gels with water. Their viscosity and that of lubricants must be high enough for them to be retained between the particles of solid under the particular pressure applied during extrusion or pressing. The choice of plasticiser or in some cases of a combination of say a plasticiser and a lubricant, for a particular purpose is something that has to be arrived at largely by trial and error, but the following broad classification into three groups may serve as a guide.

TABLE 2.1

Plasticisers, bonds and lubricants

Material	Properties	Typical applications
Group 1		
Gum arabic and some other gums.	Good dispersion agents and bonds. About 1% solid is effective	Extrusion of low tension porcelain, steatite
Synthetic polymers eg. polyvinyl alcohol or acetate	Effective as bonds. About 1% is required. Some are obtainable as emulsions, convertible into solutions by addition of alkali.	Dry pressing of alumina, titanates.
Group 2		
Gum tragacanth	0.2% is effective as a plasticiser 1% as a bond	Extrusion or dry pressing of refractory oxides, e.g. alumina
Ammonium alginate	Derived from seaweed. Its behaviour is rather similar to gum tragacanth	do.
Cellulose and derivatives, e.g. starch, carboxy-methyl celluloses	More than 1% is generally necessary as bonds. Effective as bonds and plasticisers	do.
Bentonite	1 to 3% effective as plasticiser	Extrusion of various non-plastics
Group 3		
Miscible oils, eg. cutting oils	Lubricants. Not more than a few percent necessary. Frequently used in conjunction with paraffin	Semi-wet pressing of low tension porcelain
Wax emulsions	Usually contain about 50% solid wax (e.g. paraffin wax) Good lubricants (2 or 3% emulsion effective). Also act as bonds, but up to 15% emulsion is necessary. (Solid paraffin wax is also used by blending in heated mixing pans)	Extensively used for dry pressing many types of electroceramics, particularly low tension porcelain and steatite

1. *Sol-forming*, giving fairly clear liquids, either approaching true solutions, or more viscous and obviously colloidal solutions.
2. *Gel-forming*, giving a jelly-like mass by absorption of water, accompanied by swelling, having a definite yield-point, and only becoming really fluid when very dilute or when strongly agitated.
3. *Emulsion-forming* : These are mainly oils and waxes that are either already emulsified in water as supplied, or are capable of becoming so with the aid of an emulsifier such as triethanolamine.

A selection of typical materials, with an indication of their properties, is listed in Table 2.1. Many of them function in more than one way : some are good plasticisers and also effective bonds ; others act mainly as lubricants, but also to some extent as bonds. Sometimes more than one material is used in order to make use of the more desirable properties of each. Inevitably there is some overlapping between the three groups, particularly the first two.

In general, Group 1 materials show a tendency to migrate to the surface of the body when drying, forming a hard skin which may give difficulty in cutting or machining operations. Those in Group 2 do not suffer from this disadvantage, but require more care to ensure complete dispersion and uniform mixing in the body, and they also tend to give a higher wet-to-dry shrinkage. This is of course a general point which has to be considered, as the greater the plasticity the greater the drying shrinkage, and therefore a compromise has to be made. Finally, mention should be made of some fairly recently introduced deflocculants for slip casting, consisting of the sodium or ammonium salts of polycarboxy acids ; the latter are used where it is necessary to avoid contamination by inorganic residues.

REFERENCE

1. S. Levine, *Ceram. Age*, **75,** (1), 39, 1960 ; **75**, (2), 25, 1960 ; **75**, (3), 29, 1960.

FURTHER READING

"Raw Materials", W. E. Worrall. Institute of Ceramics Textbook Series, Maclaren and Sons Ltd., London, 1964.

"Industrial Ceramics", F. Singer and S. Singer. Chapman & Hall Ltd., London, 1963, Chapter 1.

CHAPTER 3

MANUFACTURE

I—GENERAL; BODY PREPARATION

3.1 General

Many of the traditional methods of manufacture are used, particularly for clay-based bodies, but modifications are necessary for dealing with non-clay bodies. Several techniques entirely new to ceramics have had to be developed, some adapted from those used in other industries, particularly the food, pharmaceutical and metal industries, in order to fabricate many of the newer materials and to obtain the special properties required. These special methods will be described in later sections.

Familiar body preparation methods used include wet and dry rotary or vibratory grinding in cylindrical pebble mills to reduce raw materials to precisely controlled fineness; blunging by rotating paddles in octagonal-section vessels to disperse clays and to blend the body constituents (thorough homogenising is essential in technical ceramics generally) ; dry and semi-wet mixing in pan-mills ; filter-pressing ; de-airing pug extrusion ; and, less frequently, slip mixing for slip casting. Magnetting is also an important step, to remove traces of metallic iron.

Shaping techniques used for clay-based bodies are also similar to the traditional ones. For example, plastic methods are widely used, such as jolleying—that is beating the plastic body into a plaster mould to provide the external shape, and shaping the inside by applying a metal tool with the mould rotating. Pressing in steel moulds, either in the plastic or semi-dry state, is also very common, although for the latter the conditions are somewhat different from those used in tile pressing. Slip casting is only rarely used.

Firing methods are generally similar to those used for the more conventional types of ware, but have to be modified for certain materials and in some cases new techniques have had to be devised for example hot pressing.

Some of the newer techniques have in turn reacted on the older

17

branches of the industry. Two cases are spray drying, now being used for tile manufacture, and isostatic pressing, which is being tried out for producing sewerage pipes, sanitary ware and saggers. "Traditional" ceramics may thus profit by a study of some of the newer techniques, although the latter may at first sight appear rather exotic and expensive.

3.2 Comminution and blending

It will be assumed that the raw materials have been ground to the correct particle size either by the supplier or the user, and are ready to be mixed, e.g. quartz and felspar (see under 2.3 and 2.4).

There are three essentials in mixing bodies for high quality technical ware : accuracy in batching, homogeneity, and freedom from contamination. Accuracy in making up a body is vital to the whole manufacture, and an error might be detected only after firing, in which case serious losses could result. For this reason, as well as to economise in labour, the trend is to introduce automatic batching systems, of which there is a variety. One recently marketed device consists of a "load-cell" placed under each leg of a ball mill, tank or blunger ; this transmits a pneumatic signal to a meter, the weight of material introduced or discharged being thereby regulated.

Mixing is done either dry or wet. If the former, the raw materials, particularly clays, must be in a thoroughly disintegrated condition (usually less than 300 mesh size) as received, or else they must be passed through a disintegrator before use. Whichever type of disintegrator is used—pin, swinging hammer, etc.—it is most important to ensure, preferably by putting through a trial batch of material, that it will resist abrasion by that particular material.

For most technical ceramics wet mixing is preferred, as it is more thorough than dry mixing. This is important in ensuring the maximum homogeneity for high quality products, such as high tension porcelain, which will be subjected to high electrical or mechanical stress. It also minimises specking and localised structural weaknesses caused by even a small number of particles of foreign matter. The procedure is generally similar to that used for high grade domestic ware.

On the other hand some products made in large quantities, like pressed low tension porcelain and steatite are not so demanding, and for these dry mixing is adequate. This method is cheaper, since no de-watering is necessary. For materials that are free-pouring and do not tend to aggregate, dry mixing presents no problem, and several types of equipment are available. For example, there are rotary batch mixers, consisting of a drum with internal baffles in the form of blades or scoops.

Another type of mixer is the cone blender[1], again in various designs, e.g. two truncated cones joined by a cylindrical section at their bases ; and V– or Y– blenders. Both rotate about a horizontal spindle to give a tumbler action ; baffles may or may not be fitted inside. Very fine or slightly damp materials are naturally more difficult to blend thoroughly, and the answer in this case is to mix them in a cylinder mill or pan mixer, or to pass them through an attritor or other comminuting mill.

For the blending of materials in the plastic or near-plastic state, either a pan mill or a blade mixer as used for bakery doughs and fitted with Z-shaped blades, may be used. For some purposes, however, differences in physical characteristics of the material made by the two methods may cause some difficulty, particularly with material to be used for dry pressing ; this is due to different consolidation produced by the muller action of the pan mixer compared with the mainly shearing action of the blade mixer. Care is therefore advisable when changing from one type of mixer to the other.

For a review of mixing equipment for ceramic materials see reference 2.

Whatever methods of mixing—wet or dry—are used, contamination by metal must be guarded against, and magnetting plays an important part in removing small, and occasionally large, pieces of iron, both from slips and also from dry material that has passed through attritors. Permanent magnets may be used, but electromagnets are far more powerful.

3.3 De-watering

In preparing materials for all methods of shaping except slip casting it is necessary to remove part of the water from wet-mixed bodies, to a carefully controlled extent, or to dry them off completely.

The traditional method—filterpressing—is widely used. Careful attention to the operating conditions is necessary to ensure a uniform product. Control is necessary over specific gravity, viscosity and degree of deflocculation of the slip, and the pressure-time cycle. Comparatively soft centres of the filter cake are cut out and returned to the mill or blunger. Binders or plasticisers may have to be added to low-clay bodies ; this is sometimes done in the mill, so that the additives become adsorbed on the solids, to give uniform distribution in the filter cakes.

After checking moisture and hardness, the filter cakes are either stored in a humidity chamber or used directly. Formerly it was the custom to store filter cakes over a long period to mature, and it was known for a clay worker to lay down stocks of filter cakes for use by the next generation. This gave a homogeneous body with high plasticity, but long storage is now generally considered unnecessary, with the almost universal use of the de-airing pugmill. If required for pressing, the cakes are partially or completely dried and dis-integrated.

In recent years alternative methods of de-watering have been adopted by some manufacturers, to eliminate the labour of handling filter cakes and to make the process continuous. Of these, two are of importance at present—drum drying and spray drying.

In *drum drying* a steel drum, through which steam is passed, rotates slowly on a horizontal axis, and dips into a tank of slip. The slip is picked up and carried round, becoming more or less dried by the time it reaches the other side, whence it is scraped off by a blade into a container or on to a conveyor belt. This method has been used in other branches of the ceramic industry and, with varying degrees of success, in electrical porcelain manufacture.

Another method, used particularly for granulation for dry pressing, but now coming into wider use, is *spray drying*, which is described in Section 3.5.

Where very small trial batches are concerned, the slop material may be poured on to a plaster bat for de-watering, provided that slight pick-up of calcium sulphate is not detrimental. Another alternative is to dry in a basin in the oven, but care must be taken to mix thoroughly after drying, in case there has been some seg-regation of components.

3.4 Preparation in plastic form

Although most of us have an idea of what we mean by *plasticity* it is one of the most difficult ceramic properties to define and to measure, because it is complex, and the mechanisms involved are imperfectly understood. It is sufficient here to note that plasticity is connected with fineness of grain (cf. ball clay and china clay), electrical charges, and in the case of clays, also with their plate-like structure and the weak bonding between the platelets. Plastic materials are characterised (a) by having a yield value, which differentiates them from viscous liquids ; (b) by being capable of deformation without rupture ; and (c) by retaining their (deformed) shape after the applied stress has been removed.

The yield value of a paste or slip depends on a number of factors, other than composition. Some mixtures that contain colloidal matter tend to form a gel on standing, which temporarily increases the yield value. On stirring, the gel structure is broken down again and the yield value lowered. Another way of putting it is to say that the yield value decreases as the rate of shear increases. A typical case is that of bentonite suspensions. This effect is known as *thixotropy*, and it has been studied mainly in connection with casting slips.

Another effect which may cause some difficulty, particularly in the extrusion of non-plastic bodies, is known as *dilatancy*. A familiar example is observed at the seaside when walking on wet sand : stepping on to a patch of sand makes the surface water disappear, and the surface of the sand patch becomes dry. On removing the pressure the water returns to the surface. This behaviour is typical of closely packed aggregates, which are forced to open up when the arrangement of particles is disturbed by applied pressure, leaving more space between the particles to accommodate the water. The problem was discussed by Osborne Reynolds towards the end of the last century, and his observations, which are still broadly accepted, make interesting reading[3]. Another occasion on which the effect is manifested is when a non-plastic body that defies extrusion by the maximum pressure available, nevertheless becomes almost liquid if shaken ; the vibration has the effect of allowing the particles to re-assume close packing, so releasing water (containing plasticiser) which lubricates the grains. The effect is not restricted to uniform spherical particles, but fineness and absence of inter-particle attraction are necessary. It is sometimes possible to overcome extrusion difficulties due to dilatancy by altering the particle size distribution or the type or amount of plasticiser.

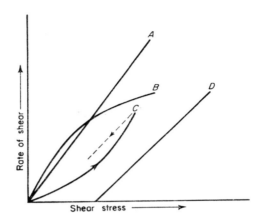

Fig. 3.1.—Types of rheological behaviour. *A*—viscous (Newtonian) ;
B—dilatant ; *C*—thixotropic ; *D*—plastic (Bingham).

Figure 3.1 represents various types of rheological behaviour.

It can be shown that a close-packed aggregate of equal spheres has a porosity of about 26% by volume. Theoretically, this can be reduced to a vanishingly small value by placing smaller spheres of exactly the right size to fit into the pores, followed by successively smaller ones. However, this does not work out in practice mainly because there would not be sufficient room for the smaller grains to move into position between the larger ones to give the theoretically closest packing. In fact the closest packing is obtained by having particles of as wide a difference in size as possible. It is possible to improve the working properties of a very fine non-plastic powder (with a plasticiser added) by adjusting the particle size distribution ; for example by carefully controlled calcination and grinding, as mentioned earlier (2.9). A case in the writer's experience was the reduction of the percentage of water necessary to give plasticity in a rutile body from 22 to 17, with a consequent reduction in drying shrinkage. It is also known that the addition of extremely fine alumina to the normally ground material, or prolonged grinding will confer a slight degree of plasticity on this otherwise non-plastic material. This, however, may be due to the introduction of colloidal or near-colloidal material rather than to particle size distribution.

Because of the necessity of maintaining consistent plasticity from batch to batch, the moisture content should be controlled to within 0.5%. Typical moisture contents for clays and other fine materials range around 22%. The type and duration of mixing, as well as the batch weight, should be standardised. One further point—if extrusion scraps are added, the proportion should be kept constant, or else they should be made up into a special batch and treated separately.

The body may be in the form of either (a) wet filter cakes, or (b) dry powder. If (a), the moisture content is adjusted by partial drying or by blending in some dry body kept for this purpose ; plasticisers, if required, are added at this stage, assuming that they are not already present. If (b), it is simply a matter of adding the correct amount of water and plasticiser. In either case thorough blending can be vital. (For small scale laboratory trials intensive mixing can be obtained by the use of rubber-lined roller mills.)

Various methods have been devised for the assessment of plasticity, of which the following are a few. A simple one is to start with the body in slip form, and to dry off in stages. The difference in moisture content at the stages when the body just ceases to flow under its own weight, and when it ceases to bind together when worked is taken as an index of its plasticity. Another test is by measuring the deformation of a cylinder of the body at various moisture contents when subjected to a specified axial impact (the Pfefferkorn method). A method has been described for obtaining a 'plasticity index' which is claimed to be independent of moisture content, consisting of compressing a cylinder to two arbitrarily chosen strains and measuring the corresponding stresses[4].

In the Linseis method the ratio of the pressure required to extrude a rod of the body to the tensile strength of an extruded rod is determined for various moisture contents. These methods may be useful for research and development work, but they do not always provide a completely satisfactory forecast of the behaviour of a body under actual production conditions ; as a production check a penetrometer is sometimes used to assess the condition of filter cakes, but in most cases the mainly subjective judgement of a skilled operator is relied upon. One piece of equipment which has been found useful in tests on the extrusion of oxides such as alumina was originally devised for research on the consistency of butter, and was later used in connection with other food products (Fig. 3.2).

The force required to extrude the material is automatically plotted against distance on a chart fixed to a drum.

Fig. 3.2.—Extrusion tester. (*Courtesy of the Food Industries Res. Assn.* ; *Nat. Inst. for Research in Dairying, and Gaydon & Co. Ltd.*).

3.5 Granulation

When fine materials are to be shaped by pressing in steel dies they must first be made free-pouring by compacting in one way or another, followed by breaking down the aggregates into granules, which will then pour easily and evenly into the die cavity.

For semi-wet pressing, as used for low tension porcelain (moisture content about 15—17%—see Section 4.7) the usual method is to crush the partially dried filter cakes in a pan mixer (unless dry mixing has been used), the necessary extra water and the lubricants then being added. These consist of paraffin and a water-soluble oil, such as those used as coolants in machining metals. Other cheap oils, such as burnt diesel oil, with an emulsifier, are also used. The proportions vary widely, a typical mixture being one part by weight of oil and two of paraffin to 10 parts of water in the body. Some manufacturers claim that it is better to add the water and oil first, followed by the paraffin, which "breaks" the oil-water emulsion and frees the oil for lubricating the die during pressing ; others, however, consider that the order of mixing is immaterial. In some cases no paraffin is used, a small amount of oil being added to the granular material before pressing. For granulation the body must be in such a condition that it can be readily broken down into granules of 1—2 mm. diameter, and yet knit together when pressed. The actual granulation is achieved by means of a "flail" type of swinging hammer mill, or some other form of disintegrator. In one procedure the disintegrated material is projected into a tunnel on leaving the disintegrator ; the coarser granules travel further, and the finer ones are stopped by air resistance after travelling a short distance. By having outlets at suitable positions along the underside of the tunnel, granules of selected size can be separated ; otherwise the latter may be graded by sieving in vibratory sieves. Another method is to mix the body and lubricants in a "counterflow" mixer, in which the pan and muller rotate in opposite directions ; after the mixing is complete, a special granulating tool in the form of a fork is fitted to the mixer, to give granules whose size is controllable by varying the speed of the mixer and the moisture content of the mix.

For dry pressing (see Section 5.2) the essential conditions are that the granules shall be strong enough to resist disintegration during handling, including automatic hopper feeding, but shall be soft enough to deform easily during pressing. Suitable bonds or lubricants, or both, must be incorporated, or added after granulation to give good pressed strength and to facilitate pressing and ejection, as well as to minimise die abrasion. Free-pouring characteristics are even more essential than for semi-wet pressing, as there is no plastic flow other than in the direction of pressing. There are three commonly used methods :—

(a) *Wet granulation*, in which the semi-plastic mix is forced through a woven screen of say 16-mesh, by means of a rocking arm granulator.

(b) *Dry granulation*, where the dry or nearly dry material is pre-pressed in a steel die, and the pressings then broken down and the granules graded as for semi-wet press material.

(c) *Spray drying*[5]. This technique was originally developed for the production of dried milk and other food products, and for pharmaceuticals. It was first used in ceramics for producing pressing material for very small ferrite rings and was later used for porcelain, steatite and other ceramics. The method consists in pumping the slip into a stream of hot

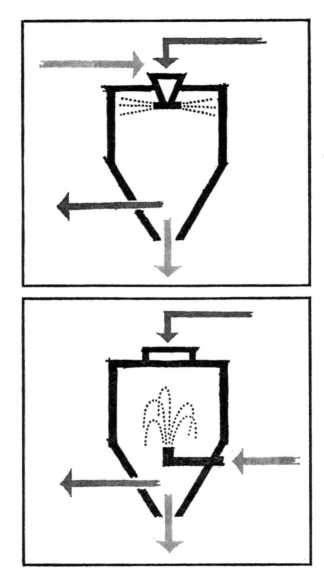

Fig. 3.3.—Spray dryer.   (*Courtesy of Cornwell Products Ltd.*).

air (Figure 3.3). The spray droplets become dried to an extent that is easily controlled, and the material in granular form is collected at the bottom of the vessel. The hot air enters from the top and follows a spiral flow pattern. Atomisation is either (*i*) by a nozzle in the lower part of the drying chamber, pointing vertically upwards, or (*ii*) by centrifugal atomisation using a rotating vaned disc fabricated with abrasive-resistant inserts, and which projects the spray radially. The former will give smaller granules, e.g. 55% between 60 and 120μ ; the latter is used for larger sizes, e.g. 65% between 250 and 500μ. The larger the size of the drying chamber the larger the granule size obtainable : using a disc atomiser a laboratory unit will give granules between 5 and 50μ, a 7—10 ft. unit 75 to 100μ, and larger units 200 to 500 μ granules. The apparent density of the granules is less than that obtained by conventional methods, and the choice of binders is sometimes found to be critical.

The advantages of spray drying are :—

(*a*) It can be used for batch or continuous production.

(*b*) Drying and granulation are achieved simultaneously.

(*c*) Spherical, free-pouring granules of very small size and narrow size range are obtained.

(*d*) Control of final moisture content and of granule size as well as of bulk density of the granulated material is simple.

(*e*) Substantial saving in labour costs is possible owing to the elimination of filter-pressing, etc.

(*f*) Saving of floor space is considerable.

In deciding whether to use spray drying in a particular case, the technical advantages may be the dominant factor, but from the economic point of view the capital outlay and cost of providing hot air (at say 250°C.) have to be set against the saving in labour. Regarding the hot air, which of course has to do the whole of the de-watering required, the solids concentration of the slip is of the greatest importance. It has been shown, for example, that in a plant producing granules at the rate of 3000 kg. per hour, a reduction of 50% in the thermal energy necessary could be achieved by increasing the feed solids concentration from 50 to 65% (see also Fig. 3.4).

The free-pouring of powders depends on a number of factors : size and size distribution, shape, surface condition, etc.

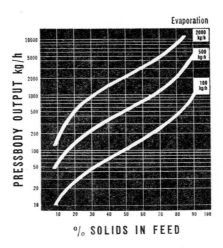

Fig. 3.4.—Spray dryer output graph. (*Courtesy of Cornwell Products Ltd.*).

Finer powder will generally give a finer texture, but will not pour so freely as coarser material, so that a compromise has to be found. The most commonly used range of granule sizes (conventional granulation) lies between 16 and 80 mesh. For very small die cavities measuring only a few thousandths of an inch in diameter, even finer material has to be produced, e.g. between 200 and 300 mesh. Such material will pour freely provided that the granules are spherical in shape, and spray drying is ideal for this purpose. A mixture of coarse and fine material will, in principle, give better packing, but the pouring properties may be impaired so as to offset this advantage. In the pressing of refractory materials the granules often consist of dense, hard particles which will not crush ; in this case a suitable mixture of sizes is essential in order to obtain dense packing, and mechanical vibrators may have to be used to achieve maximum bulk density in the die.

A variety of binders is used in preparing granulated material for dry pressing, a common one being paraffin wax (up to 10% of solid) either incorporated as flake into the material in a heated mixer, or as an emulsion containing about 50% of solid paraffin-type wax. Other binders include gums, polyvinyl alcohol and cellulose derivatives, sometimes with a small amount of wax for lubrication. The

TABLE 3.1

Body preparation (wet method)

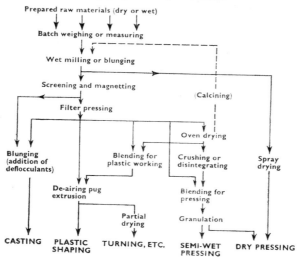

TABLE 3.2

Body preparation (Dry method)

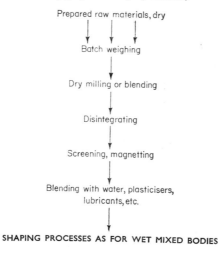

hardness of the granules is determined by the binders used, the method of granulation, and whether the material has been pre-pressed or has been obtained from reject pressings. Trouble can occur if rejects have been through several pressing cycles, the effect being that the outline of the individual granules is still visible in the pressed pieces, resulting in porosity after firing. In this case the reject pressings should be milled to break them up completely before re-use.

Tables 3.1 and 3.2 show typical sequences of operations in body preparation using wet and dry methods respectively, and Table 3.3 indicates some of the methods for producing granular material for dry-pressing.

TABLE 3.3

Granulation for dry-pressing

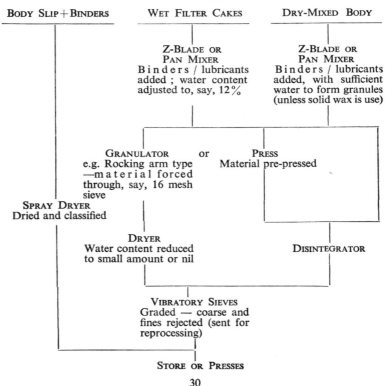

BODY SLIP + BINDERS   WET FILTER CAKES   DRY-MIXED BODY

Z-BLADE OR PAN MIXER
Binders / lubricants added ; water content adjusted to, say, 12%

Z-BLADE OR PAN MIXER
Binders / lubricants added, with sufficient water to form granules (unless solid wax is use)

GRANULATOR   or   PRESS
e.g. Rocking arm type —material forced through, say, 16 mesh sieve

Material pre-pressed

SPRAY DRYER
Dried and classified

DRYER
Water content reduced to small amount or nil

DISINTEGRATOR

VIBRATORY SIEVES
Graded — coarse and fines rejected (sent for reprocessing)

STORE OR PRESSES

REFERENCES

1(a). *Ceram. Ind.*, **73**,(2), 61, 1959.

 (b). *ibid*, **74**,(4), 121, 1960.

2. S. Levine, Mixing equipment for ceramic materials. *Ceram. Age*, **75**,(6), 23, 1959 ; **75**,(7), 24, 1959 ; **75**,(8), 27, 1959 ; **75**,(9), 22, 1959.

3. O. Reynolds, Papers on Mechanical and Physical Subjects, 1901, pp. 203—216 ; also *Nature*, **33**, 429, 1886.

4. F. Moore, "Rheology of Ceramic Systems". Institute of Ceramics Textbook Series. Maclaren & Sons Ltd., London, 1965, p.61.

5. H. Helsing, Spray drying in the ceramic industry. A/S Niro Atomizer, Copenhagen. (Obtainable from Cornwell Products Ltd., 56-60 Hallam Street, London, W.1).

CHAPTER 4

MANUFACTURE

II—PLASTIC SHAPING METHODS

4.1 Definition

Plastic shaping methods in the present context comprise extrusion, throwing, jolleying, wet pressing (both cold and hot) and semi-wet pressing : that is methods in which the moisture content is greater than in the leatherhard state, e.g. about 12—15% for a porcelain body, and in which plastic flow plays an essential part. Tolerances of $\pm 2\%$ or 0.01 in., whichever is the greater, are normally obtainable by plastic methods, and are frequently better than this in semi-wet pressing owing to the lower moisture content.

4.2 Extrusion[1]

This is widely used for producing articles of uniform cross section—circular, semi-circular, hexagonal, etc., either solid or with one or more axial bores. In the case of small cross sections the extrusion is frequently done in two stages : pieces of larger cross section are first extruded from a de-airing pug extruder, and then re-extruded from a ram extruder to give the final size. Pug extrusion is also used as an intermediate shaping stage for articles of non-uniform section, which are finally machined in the leatherhard or dry state, or jolleyed, wet pressed, etc.

4.2.1 Types of extruder

Both *pug* and *ram* types of extruder are used. For large scale production involving one type of body, a well designed de-airing pug extruder has the great advantage of giving fully de-aired, extruded ware in one continuous operation, but it also has certain disadvantages, namely :

(a) In general it is not well suited to short runs of different bodies, because a considerable amount of material is left in the machine after use, and cleaning out is apt to be very time-consuming. Small scale models are available, but the satisfactory

32

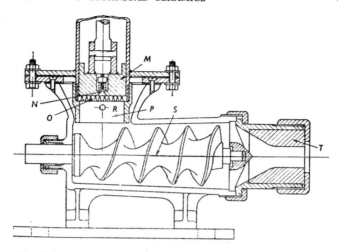

Fig. 4.1.—Laboratory pug extruder, *M* piston ; *N* pressure relief valve ;
O shredder disc ; *P* de-airing chamber ; *R* vacuum port ; *S* hand-operated
auger ; *T* die.   (*From Ref. 2, courtesy of Dr. G. W. Smith, B.C.U.R.A., and
the Institute of Physics and the Physical Society*).

de-airing extrusion of small experimental batches of less than about
a pound still presents difficulties. Figure 4.1 shows an experimental
extruder developed by the British Coal Utilisation Research Association for a variety of materials, including refractory ceramics[2].

(b)   There may be heavy wear on moving parts when extruding
the more abrasive materials, necessitating frequent renewal of
augers and bearings.

(c)   The pressure exerted on the body during extrusion is not
positive, and depends on the body adhering to the walls of the barrel
and slipping on the auger.   This means that the plasticity of the
body must be very carefully controlled—a difficult matter with bodies
that are comparatively non-plastic and inclined to be thixotropic. The
smaller the section to be extruded the greater these difficulties become,
and if less than say $\frac{1}{4}$ in. in diameter, modifications may have to be
made to the extruder to suit different bodies ; for example, the pitch
and speed of the augers and the contour of the extrusion end of the
barrel may need alteration.

(d)   A problem, common to both pug and ram extrusion of
clays and other materials with plate-like particles, is the tendency of

the latter to become aligned during extrusion, forming slip planes and finally laminations. Pug extruders are more liable to cause this fault and to produce spiral, S-shaped or other types of laminations because of the rotation of the augers.

The alternative method of extrusion—ram and cylinder extrusion —is well suited to the extrusion of small sections, for example 3-mm. diameter tubes or rods, since a high, positive pressure and smooth action are obtainable using hydraulically operated rams. Ram extruders are also easily cleaned and are therefore convenient for short runs of different bodies. The main disadvantages are :—

(*a*) the operation is not continuous.

(*b*) de-airing has to be obtained either by using an already pug de-aired blank of a size that will fit snugly into the cylinder, or by using granulated material and evacuating during extrusion.

In the latter method the ram is withdrawn and the cylinder is filled to just below a vacuum port near the upper end with the body. The ram is fitted with a sealing ring or washer, and the lower end, carrying the extrusion die, is sealed with body material. After evacuating, the ram is lowered into the upper end of the cylinder. When evacuation is complete the ram is lowered until the vacuum port is covered, after which the vacuum line can be closed. The ware is then extruded, the ram withdrawn, and the operation repeated. On the laboratory scale the extruder may be simplified by omitting the vacuum port, and making a temporary vacuum attachment by means of a piece of rubber tubing to the exit end of the extrusion die. Once the body has started to extrude, the vacuum connection is removed and the extrusion completed.

When extruding less plastic mixes under moderately high pressure the material tends to become more highly compacted towards the end of the ram stroke, and this may cause some difficulty. Ram extruders do not, of course, give spiral lamination, but concentric lamination may occur. The problem of lamination in both types of extrusion has been recognised for many years, and devices are available for minimising it, based on applying rapid vibrations to the clay or other column, in order to ramdomise the orientation of the particles just before issuing from the extruder.

A systematic investigation of the flow of ceramic bodies in extrusion has been made by the British Ceramic Research Association[3].

4.2.2 Extrusion dies

Much depends on the design of extrusion dies. It is not possible to lay down hard and fast rules, and most manufacturers design their own dies according to their experience with specific bodies. For general guidance the following notes may be of use :—

(*i*) The reduction of cross section from barrel to finishing section should be sufficient to ensure adequate compaction ; this will vary according to plasticity, the more plastic materials requiring a bigger reduction.

(*ii*) A taper is usually provided, for although even without one a material will find its own slip planes, a taper will give smoother flow and avoid the formation of "dead" areas at the entrance to the finishing section.

(*iii*) The length of the finishing section depends on the plasticity of the body ; the greater this is the longer the finishing section required to smooth out the flow after the reduction in section. If too long, the centre of the column may flow faster than the periphery, and there may also be excessive resistance to the flow of less plastic bodies.

(*iv*) For the extrusion of hollow sections the design of the core rod (sometimes called a pin or needle), and the method of fixing it in the die must be taken into account. Whatever method of fixing is used, an interruption in the smooth flow of the material is inevitable, and attention has to be paid to points (*ii*) and (*iii*). (The core itself is often tapered or contoured). Typical methods of fixing cores are :—

(*a*) A simple bridge, either straight or arched, brazed or screwed to the back end of the die.

(*b*) A multiple bridge or "spider", secured as above.

(*c*) A perforated disc with the core attached at the centre (the assembly is sometimes turned out of a solid piece in the case of very small dies). The disc may have a few large holes or a large number of small perforations ("honeycomb").

A device used for ensuring that cores are central and parallel to the die axis is a steel sleeve that fits closely between the core and the bore of the die ; it is inserted before fixing the core, or for re-aligning it, and is then removed.

An experimental tube-extrusion die used by the Batelle Memorial Institute, U.S.A., provides for the adjustment of the position of the core and of the length of the finishing section[4]. Another experimental arrangement includes a series of nesting sleeve inserts to give varying lengths and tapers, and provides for the interchange of cores[5].

4.2.3 Problems arising in extrusion[6]

Some common problems encountered from time to time in extrusion are discussed below.

(a) *Variations in cross section.* Possible causes are : (i) changes in the body, e.g. variations in the physical properties of raw or calcined materials, re-use of pugged material, variations in the viscosity of plasticisers, variations in moisture content ; (ii) variations in temperature, which may also affect body properties ; (iii) stretching or compressing of ware in taking off after extrusion ; (iv) die wear. Regarding (ii), some temperature rise is inevitable, but it may be excessive with some materials. It may be possible to avoid this by increasing the plasticity, but, failing that, a water jacket may be fitted around the extrusion barrel (this applies particularly to pug extrusion). Stretching may occur if the operator takes a long length off a vertical extruder ; and compression when a horizontally extruded length is subjected to friction as it is pushed along a board. Tilting the extruder so as to extrude on to a sloping board is useful, and some extruders are designed to be used at various angles. Alternatively a moving belt or a roller conveyor may be employed to take off the ware.

(b) *Choking of the extruder.* Here the extrusion may slow down or stop completely, the die becoming choked with comparatively hard material, while the softer material is simply churned round inside the extrusion barrel. The de-airing chamber may also become choked, since material will continue to feed in from the shredder. Possible causes are : (i) the moisture content may be too high, so that the body sticks to the augers instead of being propelled forward ; (ii) thixotropy of the plastic mix may cause the body to be very soft in the barrel where the rate of shear is high, but to harden as it approaches the die (this also occurs when initially plastic material is put in a ram extruder, where the rate of shear is low, and the material tends to set hard). The consequent heating up in the extrusion barrel only makes matters worse, and it may be necessary to stop the machine and clean out the die end of the barrel. Remedies to be tried include shortening the finishing section of the die, cooling the barrel, or increasing the speed of the extrusion auger relative to that of the feed auger. However, it may be that some modification of the body or method of plasticising will be necessary.

(*c*) *Cracking* of the ware during or soon after extrusion. This is a major difficulty with larger sections, but may also occur with small sections. It is basically due to lack of plasticity preventing the body knitting together after being sheared, either by the augers or in the die, although faulty die design may be a factor. The fault also appears as a tearing of the edges of rectangular sections, and is known in brick making as "dog's teeth"[7]. It may be overcome by adjusting the moisture content, by better lubrication, or by enlarging the back of the die near the corners.

(*d*) *Warping.* This often appears in the form of the bowing of tubes and rods before drying, but it can also occur during drying. It may be caused by uneven plasticity arising from unsatisfactory mixing or from thixotropy ; by hard compacted body or foreign matter in the die ; or by distortion in handling. The mixing procedure should be checked, and the barrel and die thoroughly cleaned. Modification of the die tapper may be necessary to avoid "dead" material from which particles may break away from time to time.

(*e*) *Eccentricity of the bore of tubes.* This gives uneven wall thickness, and may be disastrous in thin-walled tubes. The cause may be incorrect centring of the core rod, or hard material passing through the die and displacing it. Apart from ensuring accurate centring of the core initially, it may be necessary to improve its fixing or to make the body more plastic.

(*f*) *Lamination and differential drying shrinkage.* The problem of lamination, due to the orientation of plate-like particles, has already been referred to (2.6). Even when actual lamination does not occur, there are many instances of shrinkages, both wet to dry and dry to fired, being different parallel to the direction of extrusion and at right angles to it. Although steatite is particularly liable to give this trouble[8], it can also occur with other materials, for example clays, alumina, and graphite, all of which are more or less platey in structure. Further, the electrical and other physical properties of the fired ware also tend to be anisotropic ; for example, the dielectric strength of a specimen of electrical porcelain was found to be 425 and 660 volts per mil parallel and at right angles respectively to the direction of extrusion[9]. It may be possible to obtain some improvement by making alterations to the extruder, including the die, but a more promising approach, employed by some steatite manufacturers, is to precalcine part of the raw material, provided of course that this is otherwise permissible. When actual lamination occurs it is accentuated in firing, giving a porous and mechanically weak product.

4.3 Throwing

Although obsolescent, throwing on a potter's wheel is still in use to a limited extent for pre-shaping extruded blanks for high tension insulators, before the final turning operation. It is also said to help to homogenise the plastic body and to destroy the orientation patterns produced by pug extrusion. However, these advantages have to be weighed against the cost of this skilled extra operation.

4.4 Jolleying

This is widely used, in conjunction with turning, for making high tension insulators. The technique is basically the same as that used for domestic ware (see Section 3.1). Modifications are made for shaping particular types of insulators; for example, provision has to be made for horizontal movement of the tool, for jolleying deep cavities with undercuts or tapers. Great care has to be taken to avoid introducing strains, which may give rise to local dielectric weaknesses in the fired article, and for this reason stock is removed in small amounts at a time.

4.5 'Hot' (plastic) pressing*

The shaping of ware in the plastic state, e.g. at about 20% moisture content (wet basis) by pressing with heated tools is common in the United States, and is being used to a small but increasing extent in this country for the production of pin and disc types of high tension insulators, as an alternative to jolleying. The difference from the latter method is that the tool, which has been fabricated

---

*Not to be confused with the term 'hot pressing' as applied to sintering under pressure (9.4.8).

to give the required profile to the body, is heated to a carefully controlled temperature around 120°C. The top surface of the body is given a coating of release oil, and the tool is brought down to impress the profile on the material. The oil on the surface, and the steam evolved ensure a clean release after pressing, leaving a perfectly smooth surface. The method may be used to form a plain cavity in a pin-type insulator, an internally threaded cavity (by rotating a threaded tool first in one direction and then in the opposite direction for extraction), or to produce more or less the complete shape, leaving only a minimum amount of smoothing or turning to be carried out on the pressed piece. A slight amount of drying then serves to release the piece from the plaster mould. The chief advantage of hot plastic pressing is the saving in time and labour compared with jolleying or turning, but the cost of tooling makes it only worth while for large scale production.

4.6 Wet pressing

This method is similar to that used for the automatic shaping of mass-produced domestic holloware. A piece of pugged, de-aired body is pressed into a plaster mould to form the external shape, as in jolleying and hot pressing, but the moulds have to be reinforced to enable them to withstand the higher forming pressure used ; this is done by embedding steel plates in the plaster. The moulds are provided with air ducts in order to avoid trapping air, and so that after pressing, compressed air can be blown in to release the piece. Although economical in die costs, the method is only suitable for a few types of low tension porcelain parts where the dimensions are not critical ; the quality obtainable is not good enough for making high tension ware, and appears to be used only in certain American factories.

4.7 Semi-wet pressing

This is the main shaping method used for a great variety of low tension porcelain parts. It is included under plastic shaping methods because, unlike dust pressing as used in the tile industry, for which a moisture content around 8 % is typical, and where no bulk plastic flow takes place, the moisture content for semi-wet pressing is around 16 %, and the method depends on plastic flow in order to fill small cavities in quite complicated steel moulds. (For some products a split mould, or one with movable inserts, may be necessary in order to allow the piece to be ejected). The body is used in granular form to facilitate uniform die filling (3.5).

Manually operated fly (screw) presses are still used, but the trend is towards automatic hydraulic presses. The filling of the dies may be manual or automatic, and again the trend is towards the latter, which avoids relying on the judgement of the operator in achieving correct filling, but requires more attention to granulation. Difficulties are sometimes experienced in obtaining clean ejection of the pressed pieces from the die without "plucking", i.e. sticking to the upper punch ; moisture content is critical, and the correct amount to provide sufficient plastic flow without stickiness has to be found by trial and error for particular bodies and die shapes. Careful choice of die lubricant helps to give a good surface ; paraffin is the most usual lubricant, sometimes with the addition of a small amount of olein or other oils, and is applied to the die parts between each pressing. Correct granulation is of course essential.

REFERENCES

1. Anon, Symposium on Extrusion. *Ceram. Age*, **64**,(3), 36, 1954.

2. J. H. McKee and G. W. Smith, *J. Sci. Instr.*, **27, 26,** 1950.

3. H. R. Hodgkinson and F. J. Goodson, "The A. T. Green Book." N. F. Asbury *et al* (Ed.). The British Ceramic Research Association, 1959, pp. 269—276.

4. C. Hyde, "Ceramic Fabrication Processes". W. D. Kingery (Ed.). The Technology Press of Massachusetts Institute of Technology and John Wiley & Sons Inc., New York and London, 1960, pp. 107—111.

5. E. Mosthaf, *Ceram. Ind.*, **53**,(2), 70—71, 1949.

6. F. H. Clews, "Heavy Clay Technology". The British Ceramic Research Association, 1955, pp. 82—93. (New edition in preparation).

7. F. H. Clews, *ibid.*, p. 77.

8. H. H. Hausner and A. F. Naporan, *Bull. Amer. Ceram. Soc.*, **24**,(7), 246, 1945.

9. E. C. Bloor, *Trans. Brit. Ceram. Soc.*, **56**,(9), 4 69, 1957.

CHAPTER 5

MANUFACTURE

III—NON-PLASTIC SHAPING METHODS

5.1 Terminology

By non-plastic methods is meant those that do not depend, or do so only indirectly, on plasticity ; they comprise dry pressing, slip casting and various machining processes. At this stage it may be useful to refer to Table 5.1, which lists the terms often used in the industry to describe the various types of pressing ; it must be admitted, however, that there is considerable divergence in terminology, not infrequently resulting in some confusion. In both dust and dry pressing the moisture content is below the critical value, i.e. the particles of solid are no longer separated by a continuous film of water, and unlike wet and semi-wet pressing, there is no bulk

TABLE 5.1

Types of pressing

Type of pressing	% Moisture content	Type of die	Condition of material	Application
Wet	18—22	Reinforced plaster	Plastic	Simple box shapes
Semi-wet	15—17 (oils added)	Steel	Plastic, granular	L.T. porcelain complicated shapes
Dust	6—10	Steel	Powder	Tiles
Dry	None, or up to 5 (binders/ lubricants added)	Steel	Granular	L.T. porcelain, steatite, various electro-ceramics

(One could also add the type of material used in the semi-dry pressing of bricks—8–12% moisture).

41

plastic flow, although the granular particles or aggregates must deform under pressure to give consolidation, except in the case of very hard, refractory materials. The variety of shapes directly obtainable by non-plastic pressing without further shaping is thus more limited.

5.2 Dry pressing

Like several other modern methods of ceramic shaping, the pressing of dry or slightly moist granular material in steel dies was taken over from quite a different field of application—the pharmaceutical industry, where it had long been used for tablet-making[1]. One of the earliest ceramic applications was the pressing of low tension parts, in Germany in 1904. A big expansion took place in the 1930's, with the introduction of steatite-based ceramic insulators and dielectrics for the radio industry. Since that time the method has been extended to the pressing of a wide range of ceramic products particularly where close dimensional tolerances are required, for example alumina, titanates and ferrites, in sizes from less than $\frac{1}{16}$ in. up to several inches in linear dimensions.

5.2.1 Principle

Dry pressing differs from other pressing methods in that the "tempering" water has been almost or entirely replaced by organic binders.

The method has several advantages :

(*1*) It is economical for large scale production, because the pressing operation can be made completely automatic, with high rates of production, and one operator can mind several presses. If dry mixing of the body is adequate for the type of ware being produced the expense of filter-pressing and drying is avoided.

(*2*) Dimensional tolerances down to $\pm 1\%$ or ± 0.005 in. for pieces smaller than about $\frac{1}{2}$ in. are readily attainable in the fired piece, since drying shrinkage is negligible.

(*3*) Plasticity is relatively unimportant, although the harder and more brittle the powder the higher the ultimate porosity.

(*4*) With granulated material there is very little dust.

Against these advantages there are a number of disadvantages :

(*i*) For complicated shapes and short runs the cost of tooling may be high.

(*ii*) Granulation involves an extra production step unless spray drying is used.

(*iii*) The dielectric and mechanical strength is lower than for parts made by other methods, and high tension porcelain cannot in general be made by this method, although reports indicate that this may not be impossible[2].

(*iv*) If the depth of the pressed piece is more than about $2\frac{1}{2}$ times the dimensions at right angles to the direction of pressing, the non-uniform densification from top to bottom (or from either end to the centre, if both top and bottom pressure is used) becomes serious. At the other extreme, it is difficult to get sufficiently even filling for pressing pieces thinner than about 0.01 in. although this can be done by first lowering the bottom punch below the correct level, filling, raising the punch to the correct level, and removing the excess material.

5.2.2 Granulation

Correct granulation is vital to the whole process and must be strictly controlled in order that the fired product shall :

(*a*) conform to close dimensional tolerances ;

(*b*) be of uniform density, both from piece to piece and within each piece ;

(*c*) have zero open porosity and also low sealed porosity (and thus high bulk density), to give high mechanical strength and acceptable electrical or magnetic properties. Other characteristics, such as texture, may also be important.

The results obtained are dependent on the quality of the pressed pieces, on which the granulation of the body has a decisive effect. Alternative routes for preparing granular material for dry pressing are indicated in Table 3.3.

5.2.3 Die design

Die design, although of great importance, is a specialised technique, and cannot be dealt with here, except to indicate a few salient points. If a customer, who is not conversant with the problems of the ceramic manufacturer, will agree to some slight modification of shape, it will often be possible to ease the die design. This may reduce tooling costs, and in some cases give a stronger pressed piece. Generally, thin walls, undercuts, and sharp changes of thickness should be avoided, edges and corners should be radiused, and a taper should be provided for ease of ejection.   Materials used range from hardened steel (sometimes chromium plated) for pressing soft materials like steatite, to tungsten carbide, usually in the form of inserts.

5.2.4 Presses

Presses are either mechanically operated *cam* or *toggle* types, or hydraulically operated.   Generally, the mechanical types are faster, and a *multi-impression rotary press* will turn out many thousand pieces per hour.   On the other hand, hydraulic presses are smoother in action and are often easier to adjust so as to give various speeds of approach and pressing, and also to give a predetermined but variable "dwell" period during which the pressure is maintained before release and ejection.   They are, however, generally slower, and can be difficult to service should a fault develop in one of the more complicated hydraulic systems.

5.2.5 Preliminary trials and controls[3]

In setting up to produce dry pressed ware the relation between compacting pressure and pressed density should be determined in the laboratory by pressing simple discs.   The *compression ratio*, i.e. the ratio of depth of die cavity to the pressed thickness, should also be determined.   This information can be used to design a die suitable for the presses to be used, although some allowance has to be made for the slightly different weights of material introduced into the die by automatic feeds.   The firing shrinkage must, of course also be known.

In production, a simple routine control is normally used ; this consists of weighing sample pressings—a number together if they are small—at regular intervals, and measuring their thickness.   This method is convenient as a quality control, and any tendency to go out of tolerance can be quickly spotted and remedied.   The weight is a check on the quantity of material being fed into the die, and, together with the thickness, is also a check on the pressed density.

5.2.6 Problems arising

(*i*) *Non-uniform density* of pressed ware.   Lack of uniform compaction is a key problem in the pressing of powders, and arises from two causes : (a) non-uniformity of die filling, i.e. variations in bulk density in the die ; and (b) non-uniform distribution of pressure during pressing.

(a) may be due to a mechanical fault in the filling device, or to poor pouring characteristics of the powder, which is a granulation problem (4.4). A vibrator unit on the die may enable very fine powders to be pressed satisfactorily ; for example, molybdenum disilicide powder down to 600-mesh has been pressed in this way. The use of *vibratory compaction*[4,5] should be mentioned here ; in this technique only a slight restraining pressure is applied to the material, the actual work of compaction being done by the energy imparted to the die assembly by the vibrator. The method has been used very successfully in the compacting of uranium oxide to over 90% of its theoretical density, in the manufacture of nuclear fuel elements. Evacuation of the die may be useful to a limited extent in dealing with very fine powders ; for example it was found to eliminate cracking due to trapped air in the pressing of metallurgical magnesite.

(b) may be due partially to uneven filling, but there is a more fundamental difficulty which is due to the friction between the powder and the die walls, the component of pressure in the direction of pressing being progressively reduced with distance from the ram. The effect is much decreased by lubricating the die walls, but is still obvious in long pieces, and is important even in short ones, for example in the making of ferrites, where it is not only a matter of dimensional tolerances but of the effect of pore size distribution on grain growth during sintering, and on fired properties. Most of the published work on this problem seems to have been by the powder metallurgists, for example Duwez and Zwell, who studied the pressure distribution during the pressing of copper and steel powders. Of more immediate relevance to the pressing of ceramics is a study by D. Train on magnesium carbonate[6]. Resistance gauges were used to plot pressure distribution, and density distribution was also obtained (Fig. 5.1). Particularly interesting is the high density zone in the mid-lower centre, apparently due to the resultant of the vertical force and the horizontal inward reaction of the walls. A further point is that more efficient bonding and greater strength are obtained if the particles are subjected to shear as well as to compression. On the contrary, just below the ram, where there is

45

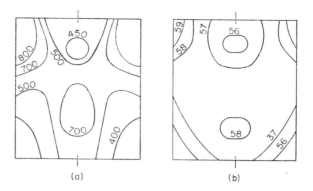

(a)   (b)

Fig. 5.1.—Reactions in compact when pressed at 671 kg/cm². (*a*) Contour levels in kg/cm² ; (*b*) Contours represent percentage of solid present. (*Courtesy of Dr. D. Train and the Institution of Chemical Engineers*).

compression only, the compact is comparatively weak and liable to the type of lamination known as "capping". (See also reference 7.)

(*ii*) *Cracked pieces.* This is a frequent problem, and occurs either after pressing or after firing. Possible causes are (a) gross variation in pressed density within the piece ; (b) lamination due to trapped air, which in turn may be the result of insufficient clearances between punch and die cavity, too rapid pressing, too short a dwell, or faulty granulation ; (c) pressure lamination, due to the pressure being too high for the particular type and amount of binder used ; (d) too rapid ejection after pressing.

(*iii*) *Attainment of maximum fired density.* The effect of the powder bulk density of granulated steatite bodies has been investigated by Berry, Allen and Hassett[8], who found that powders with a high bulk density required a lower pressure to yield a given pressed density and, since the volume firing shrinkage was not significantly affected, tended to give higher fired densities. On the contrary, finer powders, with lower bulk density, gave higher fired strength, owing to the greater area of contact. Another factor is the hardness of the granules, which was discussed earlier (p. 30).

(*iv*) *Particle orientation.* Alignment of platey particles, although generally less troublesome than in extrusion, can result in difficulty in dimensional control, because of the differential firing shrinkage parallel and at right angles to the direction of pressing. This problem is referred to again in section 13.2.2 in connection with steatite ceramics.

5.3 Slip casting

The conventional method of slip casting, with the aid of an alkaline deflocculant is occasionally employed for making small quantities of complicated shapes in electrical porcelain. Non-clay bodies, such as pure oxides, are sometimes slip cast in alkaline media, but minimum viscosity and greater stability to changes in concentration of deflocculant are obtainable in acid media, which also give good mould release. As against these advantages, however, acids cause high mould wear. An alternative is to use a polyphosphate such as 'Calgon' (although this is also reported to cause high mould wear), or one of the organic compounds now marketed for the purpose, and which are useful when it is necessary to avoid inorganic residues after firing. Another point to be considered is compatibility of the ceramic with water. For instance magnesium oxide may alter the pH of the suspension by producing hydroxyl ions due to slight reaction with water, a problem which has been overcome by using an alcohol such as isopropyl alcohol instead of water as the suspending medium.

5.4 Drying [9]

Complete or partial drying of the ware may be required : the former immediately prior to any machining or fettling necessary ; the latter to bring the ware to the leatherhard state (about $12—15\%$ moisture in the case of electrical porcelain), to facilitate the turning of articles such as high tension insulators. The usual precautions are taken to avoid too rapid local drying and too high a moisture gradient in the ware, particularly in thick sections and bodies having a high wet-to-dry shrinkage. Humidity ovens are frequently used, and the drying period may extend over several days, although much shorter period are obtained by using jet drying. A great many small parts may be simply air-dried on racks in the shop, and finally baked at about 120°C., but trouble is sometimes experienced, even with thin tubes, which tend to curl if the rate of evaporation from upper and lower surfaces is very uneven.

5.5 Machining[10-18]

5.5.1 Reasons for machining

Many machining operations are carried out on ceramics in both the unfired and fired state ; in fact almost all the methods of metal working are now applied to ceramics. With the use of modern grinding facilities and techniques, a surface finish better than 0.0001 in. is obtainable on fired ware. However, so long as the firing shrinkage can be controlled sufficiently closely to obtain the required dimensional precision in the fired ware, machining after firing is to avoided, as it adds considerably to the cost of production. On the other hand there are many products where it is not possible to avoid this ; for example, certain high tension porcelain bushings, alumina parts for radio valves, ceramics for ultrasonic generator units, and accurately threaded parts.

5.5.2 Cutting-off

For cutting off lengths of unfired ware, or of fired ware that is not particularly hard, thin, resin-bonded silicon carbide grit wheels, rotating at high speed, are used. The thickness of the wheel and the fineness of the grit are chosen according to the size and strength of the piece and the fineness of cut required ; for example, for fragile articles such as thin-walled tubes the wheel thickness may be $\frac{1}{32}$ in. and the grit 80-mesh. The grinding wheel manufacturers can usually give advice, but a few preliminary experiments may be necessary in particular cases.

For the harder materials like sintered alumina, diamond-impregnated metal wheels are usually necessary, and in any case the fact that silicon carbide is only slightly harder than sintered alumina makes diamond more economical, despite its higher initial cost. (Note that the difference in hardness between diamond and corundum is more than six times that between silicon carbide and corundum.

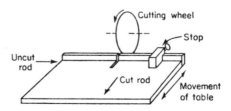

Fig. 5.2.—Cutting off tubes and rods.

Fig. 5.2 shows the main features of a simple *cutting-off machine* for tubes and rods. It consists of a steel table mounted on roller or ball-bearings which allow it to move horizontally. One end of the tubes or rods is brought up to an adjustable stop, and the ware is held firmly by hand against the back edge of the table. The latter is moved forward so that the wheel enters the slot in the table and cuts off the required length. By arranging for a gentle slope from back to front of the table the cut lengths will roll down and may be collected in a box. Means of dust extraction must be provided. A convenient modification for large scale production consists of a multiple cutting wheel with a corresponding number of slots in the cutting table, and mechanical means for holding the uncut ware in position foɪ cutting. In this case the cut length would not be adjustable over a wide range, since the position of the slots would be fixed ; some adjustment could be provided by having wide slots and varying the distance between the units of the multiple wheel.

5.5.3 Turning

Turning before firing is of wide application and is practised on a large scale for the final shaping of porcelain insulators. Some ware is turned in the dry state, where very closely controlled fired sizes are necessary, in order to eliminate completely any further drying shrinkage. Tool wear is rather heavy in this case, and the operation much slower than if the body is turned in the leatherhard state, in which the body is not sufficiently plastic to distort, but is soft enough to be turned rapidly and without excessive tool wear. The subsequent drying shrinkage is very small, and normal fired size tolerances can easily be obtained. In order to minimise wastage due to excessive stock removal, the size of the blanks should be only slightly greater than the turned size, and for making articles such as telephone line insulators and similar shapes, the body would be extruded at the appropriate diameter to ensure this. Both vertical and horizontal lathes are used. Tools may be of hardened steel, for small orders, but otherwise they are frequently tipped with tungsten carbide. Both internal and external shaping is done, and the tools are often mounted on a rotatable turret to allow quick indexing. For internal turning the blank may be held in a self-centering chuck, while for external turning a driven expanding mandrel may be used.   Usually a template of the required shape is used to guide the tool.   Automatic control is now coming into use, and the vertical turning of high tension porcelain bushings up to 10 ft. high can be automated by the use of a photocell to obtain the correct profile.

5.5.4 Surface finishing[14]

The fineness of finish obtainable on fired ceramics depends on the fineness of the abrasive grit and also on the hardness and texture of the ceramic.   Even a minor degree of porosity or of uneven hardness, e.g. as between crystalline and glassy phases, in the ceramic will give a poor finish.   A trial on the effect of grit size and of composition of the ceramic showed that for an alumina ceramic a surface finish of 35—40 micro-inches was obtainable on an 83% alumina body, using 100-mesh diamond grit, whilst with a 99% alumina and the same grit size, a finish of 15—20 micro-inches was obtainable ; decreasing the grit size from 100-mesh to 2 microns improved the surface finish of the latter body to 4—5 micro-inches. For lapping purposes the diamond grit is used in the form of a slurry on a soft iron plate, the lapping machine being fairly conventional.

5.5.5 Grinding

Grinding operations, in addition to surface grinding and lapping, include double disc, internal, cylindrical, form, thread, and centreless grinding.   Coolants are normally used to protect the work and the grinding wheel.   Speeds and rates of feed are regulated, mainly according to experience, and a compromise has to be found between the economy of high rates of production and the slower rates necessary to achieve high quality and avoid excessive wear or damage to wheels and damage to the work.   It is, of course, necessary to pay regard to the recommendations of the wheel manufacturer when deciding on procedures.   One important economic consideration is that the cost of obtaining finer tolerances rises steeply.

5.5.6 Ultrasonic drilling[15, 16, 17]

The need to produce small holes in extremely hard ceramics has led to the development of ultrasonic techniques to the commercial stage. Magnetostrictive transducers are used in conjunction with abrasive powders suspended in water or other liquids.   Frequencies used are of the order of 20—30 kc/sec.   There is no need to use specially hard tools, as the tool itself does not come into contact with the ceramic material, and brass, copper and unhardened steel are suitable.   The maximum diameter of hole that can be drilled in one operation is about $1\frac{1}{2}$ in., and the minimum diameter obtainable is about 0.015 in.   The maximum depth depends on the diameter of the hole, e.g. $\frac{3}{4}$ in. for a diameter of 0.1 in.   With deeper holes the rate of wear of the tool increases until it becomes equal to the rate of drilling.

5.5.7 Machinable ceramics

Naturally it is very desirable to be able to use ceramics that are soft enough when fired to make machining easy, or that have a negligible firing shrinkage.   Many years ago it was found that block talc (otherwise known as steatite, lava block or soapstone—see Section 2.6), could be very easily machined, and had a negligible firing shrinkage, yielding a porous product with excellent electrical resistivity when protected against the ingress of moisture.   This material has found numerous applications for insulating metal parts in electric lamps and valves.   A number of products have been developed in recent years in an attempt to obtain these advantages in other ways ; for example phosphate-bonded talc[18], hot-pressed synthetic mica, and phosphate-bonded mica.   Pyrophyllite, with its similar structure to talc, is also of interest ; one commercial product, "Alsil", is claimed to have very low porosity, high mechanical strength and high thermal shock resistance when fired to 1250°C. ; applications include welding nozzles and telecommunications equipment.   A recent development is the production of boron nitride (11.6.2) which can easily be machined after firing.

5.6 New techniques

The methods described so far have been the more traditional ones or extensions of these.   Newer techniques which have been introduced in order to fabricate the more difficult non-clay materials will be dealt with later, in conjunction with particular types of technical ceramics.

REFERENCES

1. A. Little and K. A. Mitchell, "Tablet Making".   The Northern Publishing Co. Ltd., Liverpool, 1951.

2. New Canadian Ceramic.   *Refract. J.*, **36**,(10), 306, 1960.

3. H. Thurnauer, "Ceramic Fabrication Processes", W. D. Kingery (Ed.).   M.I.T. Press and John Wiley, New York and London, 1958, pp. 62—70.

4. W. C. Bell, *ibid*, pp. 74.

5. Anon, *New Scientist*, Dec. 15, 1960, p. 1597.

6. D. Train, *Trans. Inst. Chem. Engnrs.*, **35**,(4), 258, 1957.

7. G. J. Oudemans, "Science of Ceramics 2".   G. H. Stewart (Ed.) Academic Press, London and New York, 1965, p. 133.

8. T. F. Berry, W. C. Allen, and W. A. Hassett, *Bull. Amer. Ceram. Soc.*, **36**,(8), 393, 1959.

9. R. W. Ford, "Drying".   Institute of Ceramics Textbook Series. Maclaren and Sons Ltd., London, 1965.

10. C. E. Woodall, *Trans. Electrochem. Soc.*, **68**, 111—128, 1935.

11. The Carborundum Co., *Advanced Materials Technology*. Niagara Falls, N.Y.   Fall issue, 1961, p. 7.

12. D. W. Luks, "Electronic and Newer Ceramics".   J. J. Svec, G. L. Vincent and K. A. Brent (Eds.).   Industrial Publications, Chicago, 1959, p. 85.

13. S. Boetcher, *Ceram. Age*, **68**,(5), 26—29, 1956.

14. E. C. Lucs, *Ceramics*, **16**,(194), 24, 1965.

15. M. S. Hartley, *Electronics*, **29**, 132—135, 1956.

16. N. K. Marshall, *Ceram. Ind.*, **72**, (5), 103, 1959.

17. R. Williams, *Ceram. Age*, **64**, (1), 41, 1954.

18. J. S. Comeforo, J. E. Breedlove and H. Thurnauer, *Ceram.Age*, **64**, (3), 9, 1954.

CHAPTER 6

MANUFACTURE

IV—GLAZING, FIRING, INSPECTION

6.1 Glazing

Many technical ceramics are glazed, particularly if they are to be used in damp or contaminated atmospheres, for example porcelain insulators, although there are many applications for which glazing is unnecessary. Most glazes used are of the raw, once-fired, felspathic type, applied to the ware before firing. Other types are also used, such as lead glazes, the ware then being twice fired. Application is by dipping or spraying. The former tends to be used for large articles ; for instance, 10-ft. high tension bushings are sometimes dipped in a tank of glaze slip and are handled by two men by means of a pole or pipe passing through the bushings and clamped rigidly to it. Smaller pieces such as tubes a few inches in length lend themselves to automatic spraying followed by drying, in circular booths in which they are carried round on rotating spigots. The composition and other details of the various glazes used will be dealt with under the section on porcelain (7.5).

6.2 Firing

6.2.1 Types of kiln

A wide variety of types and sizes of kilns are used : tunnel, intermittent (including the "top hat" type), and various small and special kilns. In the case of tunnel kilns the size varies from about 400-ft. long, with a setting width of 5 ft. 8 in. and setting height of 5 ft. 2 in., used for large high tension insulators, down to miniature tunnels in the form of tubes of 1 or 2 in. diameter and 1 or 2 ft. long, for very small articles. The points to be considered are : (a) the final firing temperature and the firing schedule are often critical, particularly with non-clay ceramics ; (b) temperatures tend to be higher and to cover a much wider spread than with the more conventional ware ; (c) occasionally, controlled atmospheres are necessary—for example, inert atmospheres for some ferrites, and reducing atmospheres for high temperature metallizing ; (d) there is a great variety of sizes and shapes of ware.

The choice of kiln naturally depends a great deal upon the volume of production, as well as on the price and availability of fuels and type of ware and the precision required in the control of temperatures and atmospheres. For small orders for special types of product, batch kilns are generally more convenient, and avoid interruption of normal tunnel kiln flow. If one tunnel kiln is used for all ware the schedule must be appropriate to the largest sizes ; this is not always a disadvantage provided that the relative output of the various sizes allows the spaces between the larger ware to be filled up to give high setting density. Ideally body composition would be adjusted to allow all ware to be fired at the same temperature, but this is not always possible, in which case it is difficult to make efficient use of a single tunnel kiln.

For very small pieces such as tubular capacitor dielectrics 10 mm. or so long, which can be fired very quickly, a miniature tunnel kiln may be used. One which is easily constructed, is heated by silicon carbide rod elements placed around a muffle tube. Schedules as short as 30 min. are sometimes used. It may be noted here that the non-clay types of ware do not of course require particular care in passing through temperatures around 600°C, and indeed certain types must be cooled rapidly in order to develop the required properties.

For temperatures from about 1500—1800°C. there are a number of alternatives. Gas or oil-fired tunnel kilns, either directly heated or muffle type, are used, the combustion air being preheated (maximum flame temperature of a coal gas-air mixture is only 2040°C. if the air is not preheated.) High temperature gas-fired intermittent kilns are also used, and molybdenum wire-wound muffles, requiring an atmosphere of hydrogen or cracked ammonia, are used both experimentally and for the high temperature metallising of ceramics, particularly of alumina, at temperatures up to 1700—1800°C. A recent modification of the molybdenum element furnace is the replacement of the wire-wound muffle by a number of independent wire elements which are sealed into recrystallised alumina sheaths ; furnaces of various sizes can be built up from an appropriate number of these elements.   This has the advantages that only a small flow of hydrogen is required, the muffle atmosphere is independent of that surrounding the wire, and if an element fails there is no need to replace the muffle.   These devices are marketed under the name 'Pyrotube'.   A further modification for small laboratory specimens comprises a single, closed-ended tube around which the wire is wound, within an outer sheath, hydrogen being passed through the annular space.   This forms a central element around which a furnace can be built.   The specimen is introduced inside the element tube. Molybdenum disilicide ('Kanthal Super') elements, in hairpin form and requiring no special atmosphere, are also available, for temperatures up to 1600°C.

For still higher temperatures 'solar' furnaces[1] have been tried with some success, but are naturally not a practical proposition in this country.   A typical arrangement comprises a heliostat, a plane collecting mirror, and a concentrator.   A 70-kW furnace using a parabolic mirror has been successfully used in the U.S.A. for processing high temperature refractories such as zirconia, in batches up to 60 kg.   Where sufficient solar radiation is not available a carbon arc may be used, an image of which is concentrated into a very small space by means of parabolic mirrors[2].   Both these methods have the advantage that the substance being heated can form its own container, because of the intense localisation of the heat, and temperatures up to about 3000°C. have been claimed.

6.2.2 Methods of placing

An increasing quantity of ware is now fired in open setting, but saggars are still used to a considerable extent where there is danger of adverse effect on ware of atmospheres present in gas or oil firing, and also for firing very small parts that can be 'tumble-loaded' without distortion or sticking.   In electrically heated kilns, where heat transfer is mostly by radiation, it is frequently necessary to baffle the direct radiation with silicon carbide or other refractory batts to avoid gross inequalities in heat treatment of the ware. Care must also be taken not to have a setting too wide to get uniform temperature distribution across it.   A further point is that it is essential to maintain as constant a setting density as possible, and dummy loads may have to be used when the loading is lighter than usual.   Frequent checks on temperature distribution are desirable. A point to note in connection with the calcination of various materials used in some electroceramic bodies is that the grain size distribution can be greatly influenced by setting density as this affects the uniformity of heat treatment throughout the mass of material. Variations lead to different packing densities of the calcined product, and thus to variations in plastic properties and reactivity—matters of great importance in many cases.

Placing materials and methods must be chosen carefully according to the ware to be fired. Alumina, for instance, must be low in soda for use as placing material for electrical porcelain, steatite and some electrical refractories, to aviod sticking. For these types of ware white sand is an alternative.

Care is necessary in firing most types of ware in order to avoid distortion, particularly in the case of materials of high specific gravity and short firing range, e.g. zircon porcelain (s.g. 3.6—3.9). Tubes and rods whose length does not exceed their diameter by more than about five times can often be fired packed upright in saggers. Those of greater length/diameter ratio may be laid horizontally on grooved refractory batts to ensure that they remain straight when fired. Occasionally it is necessary to fire very long lengths such as porcelain bushings and certain long thin rods. These are fired suspended, the upper ends being supported in various ways such as by passing

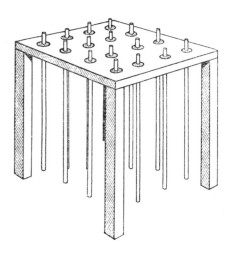

Fig. 6.1.—Suspension firing.

refractory (e.g. alumina) rods through holes near the ends, by wedging with grog or by flattening the ends while still plastic.   Fig. 6.1 illustrates the principle of supporting long thin rods from a perforated refractory batt.   After firing the upper ends are cut off and, in the case of bushings, ground flat.

If there is any tendency for the ware to stick to the placing, particularly if the firing shrinkage is high, there is a chance of cracking, or at least of distortion ; in this case the ware is fired on stilts made out of the same (unfired) material, so that there is no differential shrinkage.

6.3 Inspection

A preliminary inspection is carried out as soon as possible after firing, and the following tests are applied to almost all types of electrical ceramics.

(*i*)   A *visual check* for obvious defects, e.g. cracks and distortion.

(*ii*)   A *porosity check*.   This is done in a number of ways :—

(*a*)   A quick method is to boil a freshly broken piece of ware in an aqeous solution of about 1% of a red dye, usually rhodamine. After a minute or so the piece is removed, the dye washed off, and the piece dried ; if no dye is visible the piece is again broken to make quite sure that there has been no dye penetration.   Alternatively, the piece may be dried without washing off the dye, and again broken as before.   For dark-coloured ware a flourescent dye may be used.

(*b*)   A more stringent version of this test is to apply a pressure of say 2000 lb/in^2 to the broken specimen immersed in a 0.5% alcoholic dye solution in a pressure vessel, over a period of 24 hr.   When washed in water any sign of dye penetration is noted.   This test is specified particularly for high tension porcelain.   If the ware is glazed, any penetration of dye between glaze and body will indicate that the former is not properly attached to the latter.

(*c*)   As well as the above tests for porosity a quantitative estimate of porosity is obtained by the usual water-absorption test.

(*iii*) *Dimensional checks*.   These not only show whether a batch falls within size tolerance, but if used as a quality control can give an early indication of a change in either body or firing.

In addition to these tests, special tests appropriate to particular types of ware are carried out, e.g. flashover and dielectric tests, which will be dealt with in later sections.

REFERENCES

1. P. E. Glaser, Solar energy : new high temperature source ? *Ceram. Age,* **76,**(6), 21—25, 1960.

2. H. W. Newkirk and B. B. Brenden, Carbon arc image furnace and microscope for studies at high temperatures. *J. Amer. Ceram Soc.,* **43,**(3), 146—149, 1960.

CHAPTER 7

PORCELAIN

1—COMPOSITION, PROCESSING, PROPERTIES

7.1 Technical uses

Although the term porcelain is sometimes applied to a variety of vitreous and near-vitreous ware, it is more properly restricted to translucent, completely vitreous ware made basically from the same materials as Chinese porcelain, namely white-burning clays, felspar and silica.   It was first used in the electrical industry in the mid-19th century, and one of the earliest types of support for conductor wires consisted of a porcelain insulator mounted on a spindle.

The advantages of porcelain are that it has high insulation resistance, high electrical puncture strength, is mechanically strong, moisture and weather-resistant, and the surface is easily cleaned. For chemical applications the use of porcelain goes back further, and its advantages here include its high resistance to attack by strong acids and many other chemicals, and the fact that the composition can be chosen so as to give good thermal shock resistance in articles like crucibles.

7.2 Composition

The nominal composition of porcelain is generally considered to be 50% clay substance, 25% quartz, 25% felspar (on a 'rational' basis).   However, there are considerable variations from this, dictated by (a) the availability of various raw materials in particular localities, e.g. Bavarian pegmatite and plastic kaolins in Germany, and ball clays in England ; (b) firing temperatures and facilities available ; and (c) the tradition in different countries.   From Fig. 7.1 it will be seen that the approximate limits of composition for the three main components are :

Clay substance	40—60%
Felspar	20—35%
Quartz	20—40%

Fig. 7.1.—Composition of porcelain.

The properties required in electrical porcelain are somewhat different from those for domestic ware—translucency and whiteness are less important, mechanical and electrical properties are more important. Felspar can be reduced and silica increased to give better mechanical properties when fired, and more plastic clays can be used in order to facilitate plastic shaping. Although, as a broad generalisation the tendency is for higher felspar to give higher puncture strength, high clay substance to give improved thermal shock resistance, and high quartz to give high mechanical strength, other factors are much more important within a wide range of compositions. These are the type of raw materials used, and particularly their grain size, impurities present, and the quality of manufacture.

In deciding on the quantity of clay to use in an electrical porcelain a compromise is necessary between having insufficient to give the desired plasticity and having so much that there is excessive drying shrinkage, with the possibility of cracking in drying and of distortion in firing. More than 40% of a plastic clay is dangerous in this respect, and the total clays should not in general exceed about 55%. Increasing the kaolin content increases the firing temperature and range, as well as giving more rigidity during firing. Increasing the ball clays at the expense of the kaolins, on the other hand, lowers the firing temperature and shortens the firing range. The addition of 1—2% of bentonite has been used in order to avoid the use of ball clays, and this is very effective in providing the necessary plasticity owing to its extremely fine particle size. However, difficulties are liable to be encountered due to its fineness, particularly slower filter-pressing and drying.

The felspar content is not normally less than about 25%, otherwise the firing temperature would be rather high.   On the other hand, more than about 35% may give difficulty due to distortion during firing, and an excessive amount of glass, which would tend to reduce the thermal shock resistance.   As mentioned earlier (2.4) the particular type of felspar used (especially its Na/K ratio) has a great effect on the fluxing of the body, and therefore on its vitrification and fired properties.   It should be noted that, in speaking of felspar, a certain amount of mica is included, since the alkalis in clays are more likely to be in the form of mica than felspar.   Incidentally the fluxing power of mica is roughly 0.4 times that of felspar. Substitution of some of the felspar by the more active flux, nepheline syenite, has been found useful with more refractory (e.g. American) clays.

Silica is introduced either as ground quartz, e.g. white sand or quartzite, or less usually as flint.   It is also introduced to a varying degree by other raw materials such as clays, pegmatites and felspar sand.   The quartz content considerably affects mechanical strength after firing, but the result is complicated by a number of other factors, some of which will be discussed later.   Its effect on firing temperature and range is uncertain, and depends on the type and quantity of other components present.

TABLE 7.1

Typical recipes for electrical porcelains

	English		German		United States	
Clays	21 (C)	20 (C)	40	61	37	53
	25 (B)	35 (B)				
Felspar	34	25	11	10	23	24
Pegmatite	—	—	44	15	—	—
Felspar sand	—	—	5	15	—	—
Quartz	20	20	—	—	38	21
Whiting	—	—	—	—	2	2

(C china clays ;   B ball clays)

In addition to the three main constituents of porcelain bodies, minor amounts of other materials can be quite important in their effects ; for example, it will be noticed that in the typical compositions listed in Table 7.1, the U.S. porcelains contain 2% of whiting. This will tend to lower the firing temperature due to the formation of eutectics at lower temperatures (incidentally the lowest fusing mixture of Na, K and Ca felspars is obtained when these are in the proportion of 25:70:5). Small amounts of MgO or talc are also added to reduce the firing temperature. Traces of CaF_2 in the felspars, and Fe and Ti in the clays can also have a marked effect on vitrification.

In contrast to the above compositions, Berlin chemical porcelain, which is intended to withstand severe thermal shock, has a composition : clays 77, felspar 23, with no added quartz, as the latter would give thermal cracking ("dunting") under these conditions.

There are two principal types of porcelain, apart from the fritted "soft-paste porcelain" formerly used for artware : (*a*) "hard porcelain", as made on the Continent, and (*b*) the type made in England and America. The differences in the two types stem from the different historical development of porcelain, and the different raw materials, particularly clays, available. The type of porcelain made by Boettcher in Dresden in 1709 contained less fluxes than the original Chinese ware, and required a higher firing temperature. Much domestic ware made on the Continent is still of this type. The glazed surface is very resistant to scratching by cutlery, and the ware is white and translucent. In England, in spite of efforts to establish this type of porcelain in factories at Plymouth, Liverpool and elsewhere, in the 18th century, it was not a commercial success, and with the introduction of bone china at the end of that century, the production of both hard and soft porcelain was virtually abandoned.

Thus, with the advent of the electrical industry the demand for insulators was met on the Continent by the already established porcelain industry making hard porcelain. In England and the U.S.A. on the other hand, special factories had to be set up for the purpose. As regards raw materials, the plentiful supply of ball clays in this country facilitated the manufacture of porcelain by plastic shaping methods, and also permitted the use of lower firing temperatures. (Some insulators and laboratory ware are in fact made from a hard, Continental type of porcelain).

In spite of some obvious differences between the the two types of porcelain, they are basically similar, and any technical advantages or disadvantages in the final products are marginal ; differences in ceramic characteristics are mainly due to the different types and proportions of the clays used. On the Continent there are kaolins that are more plastic than our china clays, but they are however much less plastic than our ball clays, which are finer and therefore more reactive, thus requiring lower firing temperatures. Further, on the Continent a smaller ratio of plastic to non-plastic clays is used and until fairly recently the bodies could not be jolleyed. A summary of the main differences between the two types of porcelains is given in Table 7.2.

TABLE 7.2

Summary of differences between Continental and English porcelain

Property	Continental	English
Ratio plastic/non plastic clays	About 1 : 3	About 1 : 1
Plasticity	Relatively low	Relatively high, but lower than earthenware
Firing temperature	Prefired at 900–1000°C. followed by glost fire at 1400–1500°C.	1200-1280°C. (Once-fired)
Firing atmosphere	Reducing from about 1100°C. to end of soak	Oxidising throughout
Fired colour	Dead white or with faint bluish tinge	Slightly cream
Hardness	Somewhat harder	—
Coefficient of expansion	3.5–4.5×10^{-6}/°C.	4.5–6.5×10^{-6}/°C.

7.3 Effects of grain size variation[1]

As in other types of ceramics, the general effect of decreasing grain size of the raw materials is to accelerate the various processes that occur during firing ; the result is to give less viscous melts, lower vitrification temperatures and shorter firing ranges ; fired properties are also affected to a marked degree, as well as plastic working properties. Some manufacturers in fact control the latter to suit different shaping processes by using slightly finer or coarser quartz and ground fired scrap ("pitchers") to give more plasticity or more rigidity. The grain size of the quartz and felspar are easy to control, and are particularly important. The normal grain size of both is around 50—55% less than 0.01 mm., i.e. similar to the fineness of flint used in earthenware. The use of finer quartz results in more of this being dissolved in the glassy phase ; this in turn lowers the thermal expansion, and in many cases, but not all, gives a significant increase in fired strength. Some manufacturers claim that grinding the quartz and felspar together gives stronger products with lower thermal expansion coefficients.

7.4 Low and high tension porcelains

Reverting to Table 7.1, it will be noticed that the low tension porcelain compositions quoted contain more clay, and particularly more plastic clay. This, as well as lower quartz contents, helps to minimise die abrasion in pressing, improves the plastic flow during semi-wet pressing, and gives increased dry strength. However, the essential difference between the two lies not so much in composition as in manufacturing techniques, particularly shaping, and some manufacturers find it unnecessary to run two different bodies when only small quanities of each type of ware are being made.

The requirements as regards quality in high tension ware are naturally much more stringent than in low tension ware, and it is the high quality of manufacture of the former which is the main factor involved ; meticulous care has to be taken to avoid any inhomogeneities in the material, such as large pores, particles of foreign matter, laminations formed in extrusion, or even slight folds introduced in other plastic shaping stages, all of which can give rise to mechanical or electrical weaknesses.

(Shaping methods were discussed in Chapters 4 and 5).

7.5 Glazes

Most glazes used on porcelain are of the leadless, felspathic type, with a composition only slightly different from that of the body, and in this country are applied to the unfired ware, so that only one firing is necessary. A typical formula for a glaze maturing between 1200 and 1250°C. would be :—

$$\left. \begin{array}{l} 0.6 \ CaO \\ 0.2 \ K_2O \\ 0.1 \ BaO \\ 0.1 \ ZnO \ (or \ MgO) \end{array} \right\} \ 0.5 \ Al_2O_3 ; \ 5.0 \ SiO_2$$

In some instances a two-fire process is used, the glaze being applied after the first fire ; the second (glost) firing may be at either a lower or a higher temperature than the first (biscuit) fire. The latter is the case with Continental porcelain.

Apart from improving the appearance of the ware, glazing has other important advantages in the case of electrical porcelain. First, dirt is less readily collected on the surface, and cleaning both by rain and manually is facilitated—particularly important for high tension insulators, which are liable to be exposed to heavily contaminated atmospheres. Secondly, it helps to maintain adequate electrical resistance over the surface in humid conditions ; for example, an unglazed insulator could suffer a fall in resistivity of something like four orders of magnitude, possibly resulting in flashover, if the humidity increased from say 30 to 90%, whereas a glazed insulator, having about the same initial resistivity, would fall in resistivity by about two orders at the higher humidity. A third advantage of glazing lies in the fact that suitable once-fired glazing can give quite a large increase in mechanical strength. This is due to the compression developed in the glaze by the greater thermal contraction of the body during cooling, and also to the filling in of scratches, small surface pores or other surface defects by the glaze.

For outdoor applications glazes are frequently coloured brown by the addition of fritted mixtures of boric acid with some or all of the oxides of Fe, Cr, Zn, Mn and Al. This appears to be a matter of tradition, and the writer has not been able to discover any technical reason for it. Both coloured and colourless glazes have to be magnetted to remove magnetic iron, which would cause spotting.

Another type of glaze has been developed in order to eliminate the "corona" discharge resulting from ionisation of the layers of air next to the surfaces of high tension line insulators near the junction of metal parts with the insulator, where there is a large potential gradient. Corona has two undesirable effects : (i) radio interference and (ii) corrosion of the glaze, resulting eventually in the breakdown of the insulator. To reduce the potential gradient the portion of glaze adjacent to the metal fitting is made very slightly conducting This may seem a surprising step to take when high insulation resistance is necessary, but in fact the resistivity still remains very high—10^5—10^7 ohms per square. Higher values would not lower the voltage gradient sufficiently ; lower values would tend to cause flashover, i.e. electric discharge over the surface, short-circuiting the insulator.

Semi-conducting glazes usually contain 20—40% of mixed, calcined and ground oxides, including iron oxide with, for example, manganese oxide. The glazed insulator has then to be fired under controlled reducing conditions in order to convert some of the iron to the ferrous state. This not only develops the necessary conductivity but results in the formation on cooling of a network of conducting crystals, joined together in long chains, by virtue of their being ferromagnetic. This chain formation has the advantage that less of the oxides is required to produce the necessary conductivity ; otherwise the glaze would become mechanically weak, and inferior in surface finish.

One problem arising in the use of semi-conducting glazes is that corrosion of the glaze tends to occur due to electrolytic action associated with the presence of dissimilar materials at the glaze surface.[2] One way of overcoming the problem is to use an engobe under the ordinary glaze, containing titanium oxide, which is reduced to a controlled extent to give conduction.[3] In any case the control of the reducing atmosphere is liable to be critical.

7.6 Firing

On firing, the normal chemical and physical changes take place as in clay-based ceramics generally, that is loss of hygroscopic water, dehydration, oxidation, the α–β quartz inversion, and vitrification. Mullite needles begin to form from the felspathic melt, and also to a smaller extent from the clays, at around 1200°C. Depending on composition, quartz begins to dissolve from 1200 to 1300°C. At the latter temperature an English type of porcelain would be overfired and bloated. A body fired much above 1400°C., would contain relatively little undissolved quartz, the final composition being mullite and a glassy matrix. Little, if any, cristobalite is normally found in a fired body, because any that might be formed would immediately dissolve in the liquid phase. A correctly fired porcelain consists of tiny mullite needles, glass, and undissolved quartz ; in a typical English porcelain, the proportions would be something like 30:50:20 respectively[4]. Plate I (facing page 100), shows a photo-micrograph of a thin section of such a porcelain.

Minor effects occuring during firing include the decomposition of iron, calcium, magnesium and sulphur compounds ; appreciable amounts of some of these compounds can cause bloating before complete vitrification, as in other vitreous ware.

The composition of the melt and the glassy phase depend not only on the composition but on the grain size of the quartz, the finer material dissolving faster. The viscosity of the melt plays an important part in vitrification. The fact that in porcelain it is generally high accounts for the wide firing range (around 50°C) over which vitrification occurs. The choice and control of the felspars used is of great importance (see 2.4). Care must also be taken in making additions to lower the firing temperature, that the range is is not narrowed too much. Firing cycles depend on the size of the ware (see 6.2). Some care is necessary in cooling over the range 800—900°C., the transformation range of the felspathic glass, and, again, if much free quartz remains, over the β–α inversion at 575°C.

Hard Continental porcelain is pre-fired to 900—1000°C. under oxidising conditions, then glazed and glost fired up to 1400—1500°C. The latter firing may be subdivided into four stages :—

(*i*) *Oxidising* up to the commencement of vitrification (say 900—1000°C.) in order to burn out carbonaceous matter.

(*ii*) *Reducing* during the early stages of vitrification (say 1000—1350°C.). The purpose of this is to reduce any iron present to the ferrous state ; a uniform white colour is obtained in the fired ware, and decomposition of ferric iron towards the end of the firing is avoided, as this would be liable to cause bloating. (Incidentally the vitrification temperature may also be appreciably lowered by the reduction). A reducing atmosphere is also said to assist in obtaining a uniform temperature throughout the setting, so avoiding local discoloration and bloating. Further it is claimed to prevent oxidation of carbon and carbides deposited from the fuels at medium temperatures, as these would otherwise give off gases at the higher temperatures. If reduction has been insufficient, the surface of the fired ware develops a characteristic mottled appearance ("measling"), due to pinholes and discolouration.

(*iii*) *Neutral* or slightly reducing from about 1350°C. to the end of the soak period and the beginning of cooling.

(*iv*) *Oxidising* for the remainder of the cooling.

TABLE 7.3

Typical fired properties of porcelain

Property	Unit	Value	Factors affecting value
Apparent porosity	—	0.1 % (pl) 2 % (pr)	Composition ; firing
Apparent s.g.	—	2.3–2.5	Composition ; firing
True s.g.	—	2.4–2.5	Composition ; firing
Volume resistivity	Ohm. cm.	10^{12}–10^{14}	Lowered by high Na ; falls rapidly with rising temperature
T_e	°C.	300–500	Lowered by high Na
Surface resistivity	Ohm/sq.	About 10^{16} at 25 % relative humidity	Falls sharply with increasing relative humidity especially if unglazed
Dielectric strength	KV/mm	25–35 at 50 c/s (pl)	Lowered by inhomogeneities ; affected by conditions of measurement, e.g. falls with increasing thickness of test piece and temperature
Dielectric constant	—	5.5–6	Lowered by (sealed) porosity
Power factor	—	0.017–0.025 at 50 c/s	Increases with increasing temperature ; decreases with increasing frequency
Tensile strength	lb/in² × 10^3	3–6 (u, pl) 1.5–3 (u, pl) 4–8 (g, pl) 2–4 (g, pr)	Decreased by porosity or flaws, especially ons urface. Affected by method measurement, e.g. shape of test piece
Bending strength	lb/in² × 10^3	6–13 (u, pl) 4–8 (u, pr) 8–18 (g, pr) 6–9 (g, pr)	do. do.
Impact strength Compressive strength	ft. lb/in² lb/in² × 10^3	0.4–0.9 (u, pl) 56 (g, pl)	do. do. Decreased by porosity
Coefficient of thermal expansion	×10^{-6}/°C.	4.5–6.5 (s) 3.5–4.5 (h) (20—700°C.)	Composition — decreases with increase of SiO_2 dissolved in glassy phase

KEY :—pl—plastically made (not pressed)   g—glazed
   pr—pressed   u—unglazed
   s—'soft' porcelain   h—'hard' porcelain

7.7 Properties

Reference 5 describes the effects of variation in firing on some of the physical properties of a hard porcelain, and Table 7.3 lists some of the more important properties of fired porcelain.

7.7.1 Electrical Resistivity

Even more important than the room temperature resistivity, which is normally quite adequate for most purposes, is its variation with temperature. In porcelain and indeed most other ceramic insulators conduction is predominantly by the movement of ions, particularly of K, and Na in porcelain. The relation between volume resistivity and temperature is given approximately, over a limited temperature range by the formula :—

$$R = Ae^{B/T}$$

where R is the resistivity, A and B are constants, and T is the temperature in degrees Absolute. Taking logarithms, this becomes

$$\log R = \log A + B/T$$

so that plotting $\log R$ against $1/T$ yields a straight line. Fig. 7.2

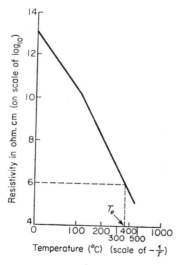

Fig. 7.2.—Electrical porcelain—resistivity *v.* temperature graph.

69

shows the type of graph actually obtained, from which it will be seen that there are two straight lines meeting at a transition point somewhere around 100°C., indicating that more than one conduction process is involved. A horizontal line drawn at a resistivity of 10^6 ohm. cm., gives the so-called T_e value, which in this case is about 350°C. It represents a somewhat arbitrary measure of the maximum temperature at which an insulator will still be useful as such. As we shall see later, other materials can be produced having much higher T_e values than that of porcelain.

Not only is bulk or volume resistivity important, but also *surface resistivity*, which is not entirely an intrinsic property of the material, but is also a function of surface condition and atmosphere. Maintenance of resistivity at higher than normal operating temperatures is an occasional requirement which may have to be met by the use of specially modified materials.

Adequate *dielectric strength* is necessary in high tension insulators, which have to withstand the increasingly high voltages used in electric power transmission. Tests are usually carried out under oil in order to avoid the discharge passing over the surface of the specimen instead of through it. The results are very dependent on the form of test piece and other test conditions, which must be closely specified. A knowledge of the dielectric strength of the material is of course necessary to the designer of high tension insulators, and it can also indicate faulty manufacture if unduly low —for example, shaping or firing faults. Breakdown occurs when the voltage stress is sufficient to cause the discharge of an avalanche of electrons, although the exact mechanism is uncertain. A distinction is made between *disruptive breakdown*, which occurs almost instantaneously, and *thermal breakdown*, which is a slower process involving an appreciable rise of temperature before actual breakdown. As might be expected, higher values are obtained by the first process, as dielectric strength falls off with rising temperature (very rapidly above about 100°C. in the case of porcelain). Under actual test conditions the process can be considered as something intermediate between the two extremes. As with mechanical strength, there may be considerable difference in dielectric strength in different directions, due to particle alignment (see 4.2.3).

The *dielectric constant* and *power factor* of porcelain are involved in calculations of power losses in transmission lines, but are only occasionally measured. Their significance in ceramics for use at radio frequencies is discussed in Section 13.1. An unusually high power factor might cause appreciable heating up of the insulator which in turn could result in instability and even breakdown in severe cases ; if this occurred in porcelain it would indicate a serious fault in manufacture, e.g. gross contamination or open porosity. The latter would put up the power factor due to moisture absorption. (Note that power factor should be measured at a specified humidity).

7.7.2 Mechanical Strength

Good mechanical strength is very important, for example high tension insulators have to withstand severe stresses, particularly in rough weather. Although tensile, impact and compressive strengths are occasionally measured, the most generally useful mechanical test is that of bending strength. Round extruded rods give more consistent results than square or hand-moulded bars, but care is necessary to avoid surface defects and laminations ; satisfactory results can usually be obtained by re-extruding pugged de-aired pieces in a small ram extruder. In firing unglazed specimens, any glaze-containing atmosphere should be avoided. Mechanical strength is susceptible to a number of variables, including the method of manufacture and glazing (note the figures given in Table 7.3), composition, grain size of raw materials, test method (increased rates of loading give increased values). Strength increases as vitrification is approached, then falls off rapidly, sometimes before the complete closing of all open pores.

Earlier theories on the effect of composition on the mechanical strength of porcelain held that the development of high strength depended on the formation of an interlocking network of mullite crystals. Later investigations showed that the quantity and size of the residual quartz were much more important. The fact that increased strength often resulted as the quartz content and fineness increased (down to a limit of about 10 microns) led to what is known as the *strain theory*. According to this, since the quartz has a higher thermal expansion than the glassy phase, the latter is put into compression on cooling after firing, thereby increasing its strength. This has been challenged, and the position is complicated by various factors, including the composition of the glass itself. However, from

71

the practical point of view it is clear that close control of grain size is essential. Note that partial substitution of quartz by alumina gives stronger and more thermally resistant bodies, but at the expense of higher firing temperatures.

REFERENCES

1. D. Beech and A. W. Norris, *Trans. Brit. Ceram. Soc.*, **60**, 556, 1961.

2. E. J. D. Smith, *ibid*, **58**, 277, 1959.

3. C. H. W. Clark, R. B. Turner and D. G. Powell, *ibid*, **60**, 330, 1961.

4. B. E. Waye, M. Ashley, B. Gibson, B. Hales and G. James, *ibid*, **62**, 421, 1963.

5. E. C. Williams, R. D. Reid-Jones and D. T. Dorril, *ibid*, **62**, 405, 1963.

FURTHER READING

"Ceramics—Physical and Chemical Fundamentals", H. Salmang, translated by M. Francis. Butterworth, London, 1961, pp. 329—349.

"Porcelain and Other Ceramic Insulating Materials", E. Rosenthal. Chapman & Hall, London, 1944.

"The Composition and Properties of Electrical Ceramics", E. C. Bloor, in "Ceramics—A Symposium", A. T. Green and G. H. Stewart (Eds.), The British Ceramic Research Association, Stoke-on-Trent, 1953, pp. 227—252.

"Studies in Triaxial Whiteware Bodies", S. T. Lundin. Almquist & Wicksel, Stockholm, 1959.

CHAPTER 8

PORCELAIN

II—PRODUCTS, MODIFIED COMPOSITIONS

8.1 High tension insulators

8.1.1 Voltages used[1]

Voltages above about 1000 are generally regarded as high tension. For long distance electric power transmission very high voltages are essential because they reduce the cross section and therefore the weight of cable required ; otherwise these would be impossibly high, both from a technical and a cost point of view. The efficiency of transmission is also improved by the use of high voltages, and the close control of supply voltages required by the Board of Trade Regulations is facilitated. In the U.K. the standard voltages are :—

(*i*) *Generating voltages* : 6,600, 11,000 and up to 33,000 V.

(*ii*) *High voltage transmission* : 11,000, 66,000, 132,000 and 275,000 V. With the advent of the Super-grid, voltages are being increased to 400,000 and 750,000 V.

(*iii*) *High voltage distribution* : 6,600 and 11,000 V.

(*iv*) *Low voltage distribution* : AC 400 V between phases, 230 V between phase and neutral ; DC 3-wire, 2×240 and 2×250 V.

For AC working the standard frequency is 50 cycles/sec. (in the U.S.A. 25 cycles/sec. is used for power and 60 for lighting).

8.1.2 Insulators for overhead lines

There are three types of insulator used in connection with overhead power lines, namely *pin, suspension* and *strain* types.

Pin types may be used for voltages up to 50 kV, but the tendency is to limit their use to 11 kV. The construction of one type is shown in Fig. 8.1. This has a soft-metal threaded "thimble", cemented into the pin hole, to accommodate a detachable threaded steel pin. Alternatively the pin may be fitted with a lead head and be screwed directly into the internally threaded pin hole. The lower end of the pin is secured to the horizontal cross-arm of the transmission pole, and the conductor cable is lashed to the groove on the upper

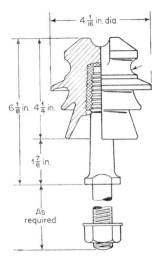

Fig. 8.1.—Pin-type, high tension insulator.   (*Courtesy of Bullers Ltd.*).

surface of the insulator. The purpose of the sheds (alternatively called "skirts", or in Canada "petticoats") is to increase the electrical resistance over the surface. In wet conditions only the unexposed under-surfaces contribute to the increase, so that the total arcing distance, i.e. the length of path that an electric discharge would have to take over the surface, is the sum of the shortest distances from the edge of one shed to the nearest point on the next lower one, plus the distance from the edge of the next (i.e the lowest) shed to the pin. In dry conditions the surfaces of the sheds are not short-circuited by a film of water, and so the effective arcing distance is much greater. Pin insulators usually flash over (or arc over) at around 10 kV per inch (dry), and that in Fig. 8.1 would flash over at about 61 kV (dry), or 37 kV (wet). Factors of safety in choosing insulators for par-ticular voltages are of course necessary, so that the voltages at which flashover actually occurs must be several times the working voltage. Insulators and pins have to be sufficiently strong to withstand severe strains, particularly in bending, and due attention has to be paid to the metalwork as well as to the porcelain.

In the *suspension* type a number of units of, say, 11 kV working voltage, are joined to form a "string". Fig. 8.2 shows the con-

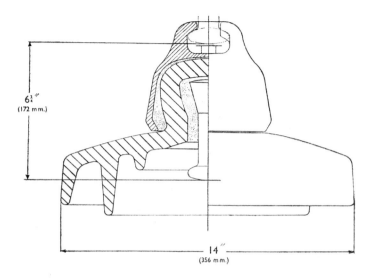

6½″
(172 m m.)

14″
(356 mm.)

Fig. 8.2.—Cap and pin insulator (anti-fog type). (*Courtesy of Bullers Ltd.*).

struction of one particular design of unit. This consists of a single disc-shaped piece of porcelain, grooved on the under-surface to increase the leakage path, and cemented to a metal cap at the top, and to a metal pin underneath. The cap is recessed to allow linking with the pin of the next unit. In use the upper end of the string of units is attached to the mast, the conductor cable being attached at the lower end. One problem in the use of long strings is the unequal potential distribution as between the various units, due to the proximity of the metalwork of the tower ; this results in the total flashover voltages being considerably less than the sum of those of the individual units. Various partially effective remedies have been used, a common one being a guard ring in the form of a large metal ring surrounding the lowest unit and connected to the metalwork at the bottom of the unit, and therefore to the line. This, in conjunction with the "horns" which can usually be seen at the ends of insulator strings, also helps to protect the equipment against the effects of a power arc, following a flashover due to an overvoltage such as that produced by a lightning stroke.

Strain or *tension* types are used to take the tension of the conductors at line terminals and at points where the line is dead-ended, e.g. at some road crossings, junctions of overhead lines with cables, river crossings, and at angle towers where there is a change of direction. A string of suspension insulators is used for this purpose, but the string is held horizontally under tension, instead of being suspended.

Various other types of insulator are used for high voltages, including the following :—

Line post insulators, which are similar to pin insulators, but are much more rigidly mounted in order to withstand high mechanical stresses associated with the operation of heavy switch-gear. For this reason they are fitted with metal caps to which the conductor is secured, and have a thick, permanently fixed metal pin. A number of units may be fitted together to form a multiple unit. Recently units with conical ends have been developed which can be fitted together with cement, so avoiding the expense and weight of metal junctions. There is also a solid core type of post insulator, without a pin, the base being secured to a shank ; this avoids the intense electrostatic forces in the neighbourhood of the pin.

Anti-fog insulators, used in heavily contaminated industrial areas. One form is similar to a string unit, but has the ribs underneath the disc lengthened to increase the leakage path and avoid deposition of dirt in the re-entrant angles. This principle is applied both to string insulator units and to pin insulators.

Various types of small insulator are made, including the Hewlett interlink (becoming obsolete), consisting of a 10-in. disc having two curved tunnels lying in planes at right angles to one another. Lead-covered steel U-links are threaded through these tunnels so that the porcelain is used in compression, the tension being taken by the metalwork. Incidentally it is sound design practice in general, to arrange for as large a component as possible of the stress to be compressive on the porcelain, the tensile component being taken by the metalwork (note the tapering of the pin and pin cavity in the cap-and-pin insulator in Fig. 8.2). Another type of small insulator is the shackle type. This consists of a grooved "bobbin" of porcelain through which a loose pin is passed, the latter being bolted at each end into the metal clamp.

8.1.3 Bushings

These are cylindrical in general shape, and may be either solid or may have a bore. They are used in conjunction with high tension transformers and capacitors, and are the largest type of insulator, some of them being over 10 ft. high. The latter are made in several sections, with skirts to increase the leakage path. Bushings are classified as follows :—

(*i*) *Solid*, with metal caps cemented on both ends.

(*ii*) *Plain*. The space between the conductor and the inner surface of the insulator may contain oil or air, which forms part of the insulation from the central conductor.

(*iii*) *Oil-filled*. Here the oil forms the major part of the insulation, the porcelain serving mainly as a container.

(*iv*) *Condenser bushings*. Cylindrical conductor layers are arranged coaxially with the insulating material, which includes oil-impregnated paper, etc., the function of the porcelain bushing being merely protective.

There are various sub-classifications of bushings, according to whether they are designed for indoor or outdoor use, or have one end immersed in oil, or whether they are hermetically sealed, etc. Bushings are used up to 275 kV and are rated according to their current-carrying capacity.

8.1.4 Alternative materials

Insulators made of toughened glass are widely used both for low and high tension applications. Advantages claimed over porcelain include much higher puncture strength, better ability to withstand power arcs, greater transparency to solar radiation and therefore less strains due to differential temperatures. These advantages, however, are not really decisive, since the design and particular use of the insulators are generally much more important. Glass insulators are not so easily damaged by impact, but when damage does occur they usually shatter—actually an advantage, because failure is then obvious, whereas porcelain high tension insulators in use have to be checked periodically for cracks, with the power on, by measuring the voltage across them[2]. Another competitive material now coming into use for indoor high tension insulation is of the epoxy resin type, which is used, for example, for making transformer bushings.

8.1.5 Manufacturing methods

It should again be emphasised that the key to the successful production of high tension ware lies in the processing—particularly the shaping.   As already mentioned, plastic shaping (other than by pressing) is the method used for nearly all high tension insulators. To give a few examples of the shaping of extruded blanks—many pin insulators are made by turning in the leatherhard state (possibly with some jolleying and hot pressing) ; solid core insulators such as post insulators by turning ; discs by hot pressing and jolleying ; and anti-fog types by jolleying.   Only complicated shapes like the Hewlett type are slip cast.   Large condenser bushings are made in a number of sections which are stuck together with body slip in the partially dried state, the process being known as "sticking-up". The lowest section is placed centrally on a turntable and other sections are then added.   Considerable skill is required to centralise and align the various sections, and the moisture content must be correct and uniform to avoid subsequent cracking.   Careful control of the final drying, glazing and firing is essential, and even a few losses at the fired stage are serious, owing to the comparatively high labour content.   Long, plain bushings are fired suspended and the top end cut after firing ; flanged ends are ground flat, also after firing.

When metal parts have to be attached, internally or externally, to the insulator, the mating surface of the unfired porcelain is roughened by coating with glaze slip, which then has "sand" (a grog made from ground pitchers or other hard material) applied to it.   Other methods, such as knurling the unfired piece, are sometimes used. When fired, the metal parts are cemented to the porcelain, usually by Portland cement, which is "cured" by heating in a humidity oven. When a slight degree of flexibility is required to prevent chipping under stress, a thin coating of bitumen may also be put on the surface.

8.1.6 Testing[3]

Three main groups of tests are applied to high tension insulators, namely design, sample and routine tests.

Design (or type) tests are for the purpose of checking that the design is satisfactory for a particular purpose.   They include :—

(*a*) An impulse flashover test in which a 1/50 microsecond high voltage impulse is applied.   The voltage at which flashover occurs is higher than at mains frequency, and the ratio between the two is termed the impulse ratio.   This test checks the ability of the insulator to withstand extremely short over-voltage surges.

(*b*) Dry flashover and 1-minute tests.   In the former the actual voltage at which flashover occurs is determined, and in the latter the ability to withstand a specified (lower) voltage is checked.

(*c*) Wet flashover and 1-minute rain tests.   These are similar to (*b*), but are carried out under simulated rain.

For sample tests samples are taken on a percentage basis, e.g. 0.5% from each batch, to establish that the characteristics of the bulk supply conform to specification.   They include :—

(*i*) a temperature-cycle test in which the insulator is immersed alternately in hot and cold water.

(*ii*) Mechanical tests to check both the porcelain and the metal parts.

(*iii*) An electro-mechanical test applied to "strings", in which electrical and mechanical stresses are applied simultaneously.

(*iv*) A puncture test, either under oil, at mains frequency, or alternatively an impulse overvoltage test in air.

(*v*) A porosity test in which freshly broken pieces of the insulator are immersed in a 0.5% alcoholic solution of fuchsine dye, under a pressure of 2,000 lb./in.^{2}, for 24 hr.

(*vi*) Galvanising tests on metal fittings.

Routine tests include :—

(*a*) an electrical flashover test, repeated every few seconds over a period of at least 5 minutes (or, in the case of bushings, an electrical withstand test).

(*b*) Mechanical (tensile) tests.

(*c*) An oil-tightness test, on oil-filled bushings.

With few exceptions routine tests are applied to the whole of the production.

8.2 Low tension insulators[5]

The distribution of electricity at ordinary low voltages, such as 230 V, involves the use of a number of insulators somewhat similar in design to pin insulators, but smaller, as well as a large number of small components for domestic fittings such as switch bases, fuse boxes and junction boxes.   Telephone line insulators are another type, used in large numbers on telegraph poles.   Then there are numerous small parts (some glazed, some not) such as rods, tubes, and bushes used in electronic equipment.   In many low tension applications such as switchgear, plugs and lamp fittings, plastics are serious competitors of porcelain.

Since the electrical requirements in the case of low tension are not so stringent as for high tension, the main objective in manufacture is economy, so long as the mechanical strength is adequate. Some types, such as shackle insulators, are made by extrusion and turning, others by extrusion and drilling or cutting, a few by dry pressing, but the great majority are made by semi-wet pressing.

Some small parts, particularly for use in electronics, have to be joined to metal parts by soldering, and therefore have to be given a coating of a suitable metal such as silver or platinum, the method being similar to that used in the decoration of tableware. However, owing to their superiority for radio purposes and ease of pressing, steatite ceramics are more usual for such parts than porcelain (see Section 13.2).

8.3 Non-felspathic porcelain

There are a few requirements for low tension insulators, principally rods or tubes forming the supports for deposited carbon resistors used in radio and other electronic circuits, where the working temperature may rise well above normal ambient temperatures. This may give rise to damage to the carbon deposit, due to the migration, under the influence of potential differences, of alkali ions derived from the felspar in the porcelain composition, with consequent attack on the deposit. (Similar electrolytic action may also cause damage to the wire of wire-wound, enamel-coated resistors, due to the alkalis in the enamel). To overcome these difficulties porcelains have been developed in which the felspar is replaced by non-felspathic fluxes consisting of alkaline earth silicates and aluminosilicates formed by calcining a selection from the carbonates of magnesium, calcium, strontium and barium, with some clay, followed by grinding.

8.4 Electrical refractories

8.4.1 Uses

Applications covered here include electric fire element supports, electrically heated muffles, various supports for heating elements, e.g. in domestic electric ovens, thermo-couple sheaths, insulating beads, and high voltage switchgear. Applications involving operating temperatures above about 1200—1300°C. are not included, as these necessitate the use of non-clay ceramics, which are dealt with under high temperature ceramics in Chapters 9, 10 and 11. In many cases good thermal shock and stress resistance is necessary as well as adequate refractoriness, and a number of different bodies are used—some porous and others vitreous.

8.4.2 Porous types

These contain clays as the main constituent, plus various refractory materials such as zircon, alumina, sillimanite, calcined china clay, and talc, but do not contain added felspar. Those containing sillimanite or alumina owe their thermal shock resistance to being grogged and having a porous structure, while those containing zircon, and more particularly talc, have a low thermal expansion—in the latter case down to about $2 \times 10^{-6}/°C.$, due to the formation of some *cordierite*, $2MgO.2Al_2O_3.5SiO_2$, with a coefficient of expansion less than $1 \times 10^{-6}/°C.$[5, 6]

Products made from these bodies are shaped by extrusion or semi-wet pressing, sometimes followed by machining. The usual maximum operating temperature of bodies containing no talc, or only a small amount, is about 1000°C. on account of reaction with the resistance wire, but the cordierite type can be used up to 1300°C. As regards electrical resistivity, the latter type has a T_e value of 600—800°C. A typical cordierite body (porous) would be : clays 75%, talc 15%, sillimanite grog 10%.

8.4.3 Vitreous types

Cordierite bodies can be made vitreous by adding felspar ; for example : clays 37%, talc 25%, sillimanite, etc. 33%, felspar 5%. Bodies of this type were first developed in Germany under the name "Sipa", and have the advantage of being self-glazing, thus overcoming the difficulty of making a glaze of sufficiently low thermal expansion to match the body.

The firing of cordierite compositions is rather critical because, if underfired, cordierite is not formed and the residual magnesium silicate has a comparatively high thermal expansion ; if slightly overfired, the cordierite decomposes to yield *forsterite*, Mg_2SiO_4, and mullite, which again increase the expansion. The presence of mineralisers, such as iron oxide, promotes the formation of cordierite at lower temperatures. The firing range of cordierite compositions is also liable to be short from the point of view of obtaining vitrification without slumping ; the range narrows progressively in passing from the two end members of a binary mixture of clay and talc, reaching a minimum at about a 30 : 70 mixture, at which point it is impracticably narrow. This is due to the fact that cordierite forms a number of eutectics with other components of the mixture, and these are apt to have fairly sharp melting points. Expedients sometimes tried for increasing the firing range are to add zircon or extra clay, or to dry mix the body in the hope that the reactions will be spread over a range of temperatures due to the less homogeneous mixing. As a result, some sacrifice as regards low thermal expansion has to be expected. Actual firing temperatures vary from 1150° to 1400°C. The fired colour varies from cream to dark brown according to impurities present, particularly iron.

For higher operating temperatures compositions containing more alumina, sillimanite or mullite, with smaller amounts of clays and with fluxes containing alkaline earths instead of felspar, are used, e.g. for pyrometer sheaths, muffles, and special chemical ware, and they were formally used for sparking plugs.

8.4.4 Zircon porcelain[7]

Replacement of quartz by zircon gives greatly improved thermal shock resistance and higher mechanical strength. A typical composition would be :—

Zircon   60%
Fluxes   25%
Ball clays 15%

The fluxes could be one or more alkaline earth carbonates, fluorides or silicates, or alkaline earth zirconium silicates. The zircon may be increased to about 80%, but the firing temperature will be correspondingly higher. Small amounts of impurities affect the firing and electrical characteristics ; alkalis, iron and titanium in particular should be kept low for high frequency applications where a low power factor is necessary. Zircon porcelain bodies are not very plastic, and die wear is likely to be heavy due to the abrasive nature of zircon and the low clay content. Firing temperatures usually lie between 1300 and 1400°C., with a range of 30—50°C. The specific gravity is higher than that of porcelain (3.4—3.8) and care is necessary to avoid distortion during firing.   For once-fired glazing a thicker coating than normal is required as the glaze tends to react with the body quite considerably.   The fired colour varies from white to dark cream according to purity.   Applications include a limited number of insulators for radio circuits.   Zircon porcelain was once used extensively for making sparking plug insulators, but has now been superseded by high-alumina.   Typical properties of zircon porcelain are :—

Coefficient of expansion	$4 \times 10^{-6}/°C.$
Modulus of rupture	25,000 lb./in.^{2}
T_e	500°C.
Power factor at 1 Mc/s.	$<10^{-3}$

The low thermal expansion, comparatively high thermal conductivity (3—4 times that of porcelain), and absence of crystal inversions, account for its good thermal shock resistance.

Compositions containing both talc and zircon are also used for making electrical refractories such as fuse components.

8.5 Chemical ware[8]

This is made from hard porcelain, since resistance to heat and thermal shock are particularly important, so that free quartz has to be kept to a minimum.   Articles are shaped by jiggering and jolleying (preceded by "batting out" on account of the lack of plasticity), casting, extrusion and dry pressing.   Articles include pipework, valves, cocks, pump parts, towers, filters, funnels, ball mill linings and grinding balls, pestles and mortars, reaction vessels, crucibles, etc.

The principal tests carried out on chemical ware are porosity, thermal shock resistance (from 250°C. to water at 15°C.), constancy of weight, heat resistance of the glaze, and resistance to acids and alkalis at 100°C. for 4 hours[9].

REFERENCES

1.   H. Cotton, "The Transmission and Distribution of Electrical Energy". English Universities Press, London, 1958, Chapter 10.
2.   A. E. Holden *et al*, *J. Inst. Electr. Eng.*, **87**, 625, 1940.

3. B.S. 137 : 1960. Porcelain and Toughened Glass Insulators for Overhead Power Lines.
   B.S. 3297 : 1960. High Voltage Post Insulators.
   B.S. 223 : 1956. High Voltage Bushings.
4. M. D. Rigterink, *Ceram. Age*, **63**,(1), 10, 1954.
5. R. S. Lamar and M. F. Warner, *J. Amer. Ceram. Soc.*, **37**,(12), 602, 1954.
6. E. C. Bloor, "Ceramics—A Symposium". A. T. Green and G. H. Stewart (Eds.), The British Ceramic Research Association, Stoke-on-Trent, 1953, p. 253.
7. E. C. Bloor, *ibid*, p. 264.
8. Anon., Laboratory Porcelain, *Ceramics*, **4**,(41), 201, 1952.
9. B.S. 914 : 1952. Quality of Laboratory Porcelain.

CHAPTER 9

HIGH TEMPERATURE CERAMICS

I—PROPERTIES, FABRICATION METHODS

9.1 Refractoriness

We now have to consider what may be described as "super duty" ceramics, for use at much higher temperatures, and under very severe conditions. It should be pointed out, however, that the quest for outstanding mechanical and thermal stability is not confined to high temperature properties, and many of the factors involved are common to both normal and high temperatures.

The materials discussed in the last two sections are multiphase ceramics, the refractory crystalline phases being bonded by a much less refractory glassy phase. In vitreous ware this forms a substantial proportion of the whole, and is a source of mechanical weakness and deterioration of electrical properties, particularly under severe conditions. In making high duty ceramics it is necessary not only to avoid quartz with its associated thermal cracking, but also to eliminate the glassy phase, or to reduce it to a minimum. The result is illustrated by zircon porcelain, the operating temperature of which can be increased to about 1450°C. by reducing the glass to a comparatively small proportion. Again, by increasing the percentage of Al_2O_3 in an alumina ceramic from 86 to 96% the maximum temperature for continuous use can be raised from 1400 to 1680°C. ; and by eliminating glass entirely and using recrystallised alumina the operating temperature can be raised to over 1900°C. We are thus concerned here with virtually non-clay, self-bonded ceramics. Even so, there must clearly be a gap between the melting point and the maximum temperature of use, depending on the conditions of service—particularly mechanical loading, as in the more conventional metallurgical refractories—and this must influence our assessment of refractoriness.

9.2 Mechanical properties[1]

The great importance attached to making available refractory materials of high strength has resulted in the development of ceramics having compressive strengths up to 600,000 lb./in.^{2} and transverse strengths of the order of 100,000 lb./in.^{2}.

The ultimate mechanical strength theoretically obtainable depends upon interatomic bond strength, whether ionic or covalent. This is favoured by smallness and closeness of packing of the atoms, and where the bonding is ionic, on the valency. The high strength of diamond is due to the small size of the carbon atom and its close (cubic) packing. In compounds having *interstitial structures*, where one atom is fitted into a network of other atoms to give close packing, high strength results, as in alumina (Al in an O framework), and titanium carbide (Ti in a C framework). Melting and boiling points are a rough indication of the strength of interatomic bonding, and there is a qualitative relation between thermal stability and mechanical strength ; there is also a rough correlation with thermal expansion.

Modulus of elasticity is closely related to mechanical strength and is often used as an indication of the latter, since it does not involve a destructive test. As a class, ceramics have higher moduli than other materials—of the order of 10^7 lb./in.^{2}.

The compressive strength of ceramics is very much higher than their tensile or their bending strength because non-ductile materials do not fail by slip, and failure by pure compression is impossible.

The maximum strength obtainable in a material is when it is in the form of a single crystal, and very high bending strengths (up to 10^6 lb./in.^{2}) have been obtained, for example, by growing single crystals of alumina, and there is great interest in single crystal whiskers of various refractory compounds. Somewhat lower strengths than would be expected on theoretical grounds are obtained in practice, as actual single crystals all contain certain imperfections. These may take a number of forms, such as dislocations of various kinds and defect structures. The study of the former falls outside the scope of this book, but it may be noted that imperfections due to the mismatching that occurs where crystals with different orientations form a grain boundary are of particular interest in ceramics because they may stabilise dislocations and so prevent further deformation.

The flow processes that take place in normally brittle materials such as refractories, glasses and brittle metals are of great interest. Any material subjected to a continuously increasing load will eventually either flow or fracture. With brittle materials deformation is almost entirely elastic up to the breaking strain, which rarely exceeds about 0.001 in ceramics. However, certain ceramic materials in the form of single crystals are inherently plastic. This plasticity depends on the ability of the crystal to slip as the result of internal dislocations. The mechanism leading to plasticity can also lead to the nucleation of small cracks ; these may then grow until they reach a critical size (Griffith cracks) or become so numerous that they join up. In either case fracture will result. The refractory material most studied in this connection is single crystal magnesium oxide, which can be prepared so as to be capable of being bent through an angle of as much as 15°. It has a similar structure (face-centred cubic) to sodium chloride, and studies of the latter, which also shows this behaviour, can be applied to magnesium oxide.

Another related mechanical property is *hardness*, which is, however, defined in different ways according to whether one is concerned with resistance to crushing, i.e. volume hardness, or to penetration, scratching or abrasion, which are to a degree surface properties. Ceramics vary in hardness from one extreme to another: some are comparable to diamond, others are soft enough to be cut with a hacksaw after firing.

Modulus of elasticity, hardness, impact resistance, ductility, fatigue and creep are of course closely bound up with crystal structure and the number and type of defects present, as well as by micro- and macrostructure.

Defect structures are important also in connection with sintering and with electrical properties, and are formed by the substitution in the crystal lattice of ions of different valency. This produces "built-in" vacancies due to the removal of a number of ions in order to maintain electrical neutrality. This topic will be referred to later.

Although dislocation theory has been successfully applied to the study of metals and single crystal ceramics, the complexities of polycrystalline ceramics, with which we are almost entirely concerned have so far prevented the achievement of any significant results in this field. While bearing in mind the importance of intrinsic factors in determining mechanical and other properties of ceramics, we must therefore concentrate on factors which are involved in fabrication, and which are to a large extent under our control.

Porosity is one of the most important factors affecting mechanical strength. It has been found that a number of ceramics obey the relation :

$$s = s_o e^{-kp}$$

where s is the strength, s_o the strength at zero porosity, p the fractional porosity, and k is a constant.

Another important factor is the final *crystal size*, which should be as small as possible, since it has been shown that strength is proportional to $1/\sqrt{d}$ where d is the crystal or grain diameter. The strength of polycrystalline materials falls off with increasing temperature—rapidly above a certain point.

9.3 Thermal properties[2]

Thermal conductivity in electrically insulating ceramics is mainly by lattice vibrations since, unlike metals they contain few free electrons. It depends on the intrinsic properties of the material, i.e. on atomic and microstructure, and decreases with impurity content, residual porosity and temperature. Porosity has an even more serious effect than impurities, and this is another reason why it is important to achieve the maximum possible density for many applications.

Thermal expansion is mainly a function of atomic and crystal structure, particularly interatomic bonding and closeness of atomic packing. It may be noted that loosely packed structures like glasses allow expansion to take place "internally", and have a comparatively low coefficient of expansion. The latter is often the most important single factor influencing thermal shock resistance and there is considerable interest in the use of lithium compounds in a variety of ceramic products for reducing their thermal expansion. Some lithium minerals, for example eucryptite ($Li_2O.Al_2O_3.2SiO_2$), spodumene ($Li_2O.Al_2O_3.4SiO_2$), and petalite ($Li_2O.Al_2O_3.8SiO_2$), have negative coefficients, and by suitable compounding, ceramics having virtually zero coefficients, and consequently excellent thermal shock resistance, have been produced[3]. Negative thermal expansion is rare, and is believed to be due to a change in atomic co-ordination from open to close packing. Another compound with a negative thermal expansion (from −180°C. to room temperature) is aluminium titanate ($Al_2O_3.TiO_2$).

One of the most difficult properties to obtain is *resistance to thermal shock and stress.* In the first place precise evaluation is difficult, for two reasons : the problem of detecting the first onset of damage, and the fact that the method of testing has a major effect on the result. Various techniques have been devised for detecting damage, but there does not appear to be any threshold value that would distinguish a damaged from an undamaged specimen ; consequently some arbitrary criterion has to be used, e.g. the number of temperature cycles between given extremes required to reduce the bending strength by 10%. Quenching may be done in air, water, or some other medium, or fluidised beds may be used as heat exchangers. However, in spite of these difficulties, by using some simplifying assumptions it is possible to make a rough assessment of the thermal shock resistance of materials ; for example, those required for high velocity military and space craft, and turbine and nuclear reactor parts. If the shape of test piece and the heat transfer coefficient (rate of heat transferred per unit area per unit temperature difference)—both important factors—are kept constant, the maximum temperature difference $\triangle T$, known as the spalling resistance index, that can be withstood is proportional to $kS/\alpha E$, where k is the thermal conductivity, S the strength, E the modulus of elasticity, and α the coefficient of thermal expansion. From this it will be apparent that the aim should be to produce a material of high thermal conductivity and strength, with a low modulus of elasticity and thermal expansion.

Considering the effect of these four factors, the following points should be noted. Thermal conductivity falls off at different rates with increasing temperature in different materials—more rapidly in most ceramics than in metals. The effect of different rates of fall-off is shown by comparing the thermal shock resistance of beryllium oxide and alumina. The former is much better at moderate temperatures, but due to a more rapid decrease in thermal conductivity (10 times that of alumina at room temperature) with increasing temperature it is little better than alumina at high temperatures. The reason for wanting a low modulus of elasticity is, of course, that a comparatively large strain can be withstood for a given stress.   However, because of the close connection between this property and mechanical strength, an increase in the latter means an increase in the modulus as well, and the effects tend to cancel one another.

The relation given above, of thermal shock resistance to the four fundamental properties, only holds, as already indicated, under specified test conditions, and has to be modified for thick specimens and high heat transfer coefficients such as exist in severe quenching. The following test figures illustrate the effect of the latter in the case of dense alumina and beryllia specimens[4]:

	Maximum temperature (°C.) from which specimens could be quenched into.	
	air	water*
Alumina	538	510
Beryllia	774	427

*Actually, quenching from high temperature into water is not to be recommended owing to the uncertainties associated with the 'cushion' of steam which is formed.

With these provisos in mind, some of the more important types of ceramics may be placed in the following approximate order of increasing thermal shock resistance :—steatite, porcelain, alumina, beryllia, silicon carbide, zircon, cordierite, fused silica, hot pressed silicon nitride.

9.4 Special methods of fabrication

9.4.1 Principal methods

Adaptations of the more traditional processes have already been dealt with in Chapters 4 and 5.   The more important of the newer techniques introduced to enable non-clay ceramics to be fabricated are :—

self attrition
isostatic pressing
injection moulding
thin (paint) film technique

reaction sintering
hot pressing (pressure sintering)
and ceramic coating methods, particularly
   flame spraying
   pyrolytic deposition.

Some of these methods are applicable not only to high temperature ceramics but to electrical and magnetic ceramics ; the thin
film technique for instance was developed first for barium titanate
ceramics. It should be noted that it is possible, e.g. in some alumina
ceramics, to obtain an increase in strength by *thermal conditioning,*
that is by reheating nearly to the maturing temperature and then
quenching.

9.4.2 Self attrition

Contamination, even to a very small degree, may adversely
affect the properties of high duty ceramics, and special precautions
have to be taken against this. Starting materials may be either
chemically purified or synthetic compounds ; some of the former,
like hydroxides and carbonates for producing pure oxide ceramics,
have to be carefully calcined and then milled to a specified grain
size. Rubber-lined mills with grinding media of approximately the
same composition as the material to be ground are frequently used ;
also steel mills and steel balls may be used, provided that the milled
material is extracted with hydrochloric acid to remove traces of iron.

An alternative is to use the principle of self attrition, in which
the grinding is done by multiple high speed impacts between the
particles themselves. The equipment used for this purpose is
known as the *fluid energy mill,* the principle of which is shown in
Fig. 9.1. The material to be ground is introduced with an air
blast into the annular duct. Another air supply is connected to
the manifold, causing a swirling air current from the jets, which are
aimed tangentially at the circumference of the imaginary circle. As
a result the solid particles are made to collide with one another. The
material is subjected to two opposing forces—(*a*) a centrifugal force
due to the swirling air from the jets, and (*b*) surface drag due to the
inward flow of air towards the central duct, through which the air
is finally discharged together with the finely ground material. So
long as the size of a particle exceeds a certain value (*a*) will predominate ; at smaller sizes (*b*) will predominate and the material

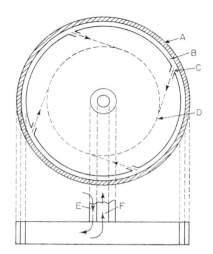

Fig. 9.1.—Fluid energy mill.   A—steel drum, 12 in. diameter ; B—manifold ;
C—jets ; D—imaginary circle, 8 in. diameter ; E—annular duct ; F—central
duct.

will be discharged via the central duct.   A small unit of this type,
used for the manufacture of sparking plug insulators to break down
aggregates of 3 micron size alumina, had a drum of 12 in. diameter
and an internal height of $1\frac{3}{4}$ in.   Even with this small size a through-
put of over 50 kg. per hour could be obtained, for an air consumption
of 250—300 ft.[3] per minute (equivalent to about 60 hp.[6]).   The
advantages of this method are : (*i*) no other grinding medium than
the material to be ground is present, and there is a minimum of
contact between material and metal surfaces, thus minimising the
chance of contamination ; (*ii*) there are no moving parts ; and (*iii*)
the process is continuous.

9.4.3 Isostatic pressing[7]

This method, used both in ceramics and powder metallurgy,
was adapted more than 20 years ago to the automatic pressing of
alumina sparking plug insulators.   More recently it has been
applied to a variety of other refractory products because, while the
small proportion of binder required gives negligible drying shrinkage,
greater uniformity of densification is obtainable compared with dry

pressing and other conventional methods. In principle, uniform pressure is applied via a fluid to a rubber or other flexible container, which is filled with the powder to be pressed. The fluid may be water, in which case the method is known as hydrostatic pressing. A simple form of equipment, suitable for pressing cylindrical shapes, consists of a compressed air cylinder operating at pressures of up to about 100 lb./in.^{2}. A piston transmits and magnifies the pressure as it is forced into a smaller steel cylinder containing water, the final pressure being up to 1 ton/in^2. This pressure is applied to a rubber bag sealed into the cylinder and containing the material to be pressed. This may be in the form of damp "dust" as used in tile pressing, but for the best results should be properly granulated, e.g. by spray drying, and contain wax or other suitable binders as for dry pressing. The piece is afterwards given its correct external profile by turning or some other machining process. The necessity for this step is a disadvantage of isostatic pressing, but the amount of material to be removed after pressing can be minimised by using shaped flexible moulds, which also allow more complex shapes to be formed. Fig. 9.2 shows equipment used for pressing spark plug insulators.

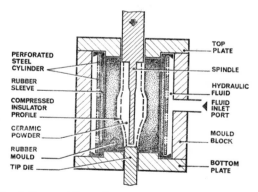

Fig. 9.2.—Isostatic moulding of spark plugs. (*Courtesy of A.C. Delco Division of General Motors Ltd.*).

A later development is the use of a reversible gel, based on polyvinyl chloride, to make moulds of the exact profile required. In this way it has been possible to produce pieces having a satisfactory size tolerance after firing, without any additional shaping after pressing [8].

Although isostatic pressing may appear at first sight to be somewhat slow, as many as 1500 pieces per hour can be produced by an automatically filled and operated press making sparking plug insulators. For high pressures glycerol is sometimes used as the compressing fluid. Pressures up to 100,000 lb./in² have been applied, the rubber container being replaced by a perforated metal tube. There are numerous other modifications of the method ; for example, crucible shapes can be made on a laboratory scale by compressing the material around a rubber stopper instead of inside a rubber bag[9]. Isostatic pressing is also used for the further densification of compacts already formed by some other method ; this has been successfully used, for example in making nose cones (radomes) for rockets. Other products include uranium oxide fuel rods and alumina grinding balls ; in the latter case the powder is introduced through a hole in a rubber ball, which is then placed in a container for isostatic pressing.

9.4.4 Injection moulding[10]

This technique, familiar in the plastics industry, has been adapted to the fabrication of irregular shaped ceramic articles by injecting a paste containing 10—20% of a synthetic resin such as polystyrene or phenol formaldehyde, into a split steel mould. After heating at 120—150°C., the piece is removed and fired. The disadvantage of the method is the high firing shrinkage due to the large amount of binder to be burned out, but it is useful for shaping rapidly in one operation pieces that would otherwise require considerable labour.

9.4.5 Thin film technique[11]

In this method a "paint" is made up composed of, say, 65% of the ceramic powder and 35% of a 5—10% solution of cellulose acetate in acetone, plus other solvents and plasticisers as normally used in cellulose paints. The paint is allowed to flow on to a slowly moving steel belt, the thickness and width of coating being determined by a doctor blade and gate, both controlled by micrometer screws. The belt carrying the paint film passes under a series of infra-red lamps, and the film is finally taken off on to a spool of fairly large diameter, and can be cut to any required size. Thicknesses down to 0.005 in. are readily achieved.

9.4.6 Sintering

Owing to the importance of fabricating most of the high-duty ceramics with as high a density as possible, the mechanism of sintering in the absence of a liquid phase has been the subject of many studies in recent years[12]. Much of the knowledge stems from powder metallurgy. A few points of particular significance from a practical aspect will now be considered.

The driving force in producing sintering is surface tension, which acts so as to reduce the surface energy of the compact to a minimum, by the elimination of internal surfaces, i.e. by reducing porosity and increasing grain size. It is found that most substances begin to sinter at a temperature approximately two-thirds of their melting point in °K.

As a result of observations, first on metals and later on ceramics, on the growth of the "neck" of material formed between two adjacent particles during sintering, it is generally accepted that the principal mechanism by which material is transported is volume diffusion of atoms or ions through the crystals into the pores, and the corresponding diffusion of the vacancies so created into "sinks" formed by crystal boundaries. As long as the crystals remain small and numerous the vacancies can reach the sinks relatively easily, but in the later stages of sintering giant crystals tend to grow (discontinuous grain growth) and to trap many pores inside them, so preventing further densification. By making certain additions it has been found possible either to inhibit discontinuous grain growth (of grain refinement in metals) or to accelerate sintering so that the large crystals do not have time to grow. An example is the addition of about 1 % of magnesium oxide to alumina (as little as 0.25 % may be effective) ; in this way, by keeping the crystal size very small, and eliminating virtually all porosity, translucent pieces of high mechanical strength can be made, e.g. "Lucalox". As mentioned in Section 9.2, both small crystal size and very low porosity are important factors making for high mechanical strength.

The rate of sintering is influenced by many factors, of which the following are some of the more important :—

(a) Increasing the area of contact between the particles, by using finer material suitably graded to give close packing, and compacting to a high pressed density, which increases the rate of sintering.

(*b*)　The rate of sintering falls off with time at a given temperature, so that a limiting density is reached, which can only be exceeded by raising the temperature, other factors remaining the same.

(*c*)　The application of pressure during sintering (hot pressing), which augments the surface energy of the particles, and accelerates sintering, with the possibility of plastic flow as well as volume diffusion occuring.

(*d*)　Defects in the crystal lattice (Section 9.2).　These enable the ions to move more freely and thus promote sintering.　They can be introduced for example by adding 1 or 2 % of titanium oxide into alumina ; since a 4-valent ion (Ti) is made to replace 3-valent Al, cation spaces must remain in order to restore electrical neutrality, with three Ti's replacing four Al's.　The ionic sizes of the two cations must of course be similar if such replacement is to be possible One problem is that crystal growth is also likely to be increased, and so the final result may not necessarily be advantageous.

(*e*)　The atmosphere during sintering often has considerable effect, particularly, but not only, where compounds of variable stoichiometry are concerned, such as zinc oxide and uranium oxide.

9.4.7 Reaction sintering[13]

Certain very hard compounds, which are otherwise difficult to fabricate in a completely dense form, are sometimes formed by the reaction of their components or of other substances that will yield the required compound, during the actual sintering of the articles ; for example, compacts of silicon are sintered in nitrogen to form dense (self-sintered) silicon nitride.

9.4.8 Hot pressing (pressure sintering)[14]

The application of pressure during sintering has been used for many years in powder metallurgy, for example for sintering carbide tool tips.　In metallurgy the main object is to increase the rate of production, but in ceramics this is secondary, the main object being to obtain a high sintered density at a moderate temperature. Ordinary sintering, without applied pressure, in many cases still leaves several percent of sealed pores in the product.　This is not only due to the difficulty of obtaining sufficiently high temperatures, but also because even if the temperature is high enough, exaggerated grain growth prevents the attainment of full densification. Hot pressing, on the other hand, will eliminate the residual porosity rapidly and almost entirely, before the onset of exaggerated grain growth. It has been estimated that the force due to the free surface energy of particles from 5 to 50 microns size is between 15 and 100 lb./in.^{2}, so that with an applied pressure of 2000 lb./in.^{2} the increase in the force acting on the surfaces is between 20 and 130 times. Fig. 9.3 illustrates the effect of hot pressing on the densification of beryllium oxide.

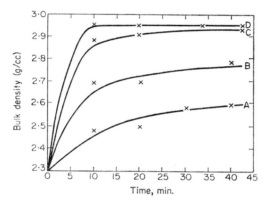

Fig. 9.3.—Densification of BeO by hot pressing. A—sintered at 1600°C.; B—sintered at 1800°C.; C—hot pressed at 1600°C. (2000 lb/in.^{2}); D—hot pressed at 1800°C. (2000 lb/in.^{2}). (Reprinted from The Hot Pressing of Ceramics, by P. Murray, D. T. Livey and J. Williams; "Ceramic Fabrication Processes", edited by W. D. Kingery. *Courtesy of the M.I.T. Press. Copyright 1958 by The Massachusetts Institute of Technology*).

A nearly theoretical density is attainable in a matter of minutes although final densification may require a longer time. and the method also has the advantage that the preparation of the material e.g. by calcining and grinding to give a specified particle size distribution, is usually less critical than in conventional sintering.

The powder, or in some cases the preformed compact, is placed in a graphite die, and pressure is applied by a graphite plunger, the die being heated either directly by passing a high current, at a low voltage, through the die itself, or indirectly by high frequency induction (see Fig. 9.4). The use of graphite dies restricts the pressure that can be applied to about 10,000 lb/in.^{2}, but higher

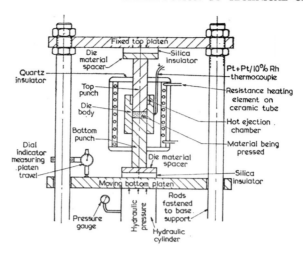

Fig. 9.4.—Schematic design of unit for the pressure-sintering (hot pressing)
of ceramic materials. (*Proc. Brit. Ceram. Soc.*, (3), 196, 1965).
(*Courtesy of Dr. T. Vasilos and the British Ceramic Society*).

pressures have recently been employed by using non-graphite dies ;
in fact hot pressing at 250,000—500,000 lb./in.², has been reported.
Pressing at temperatures low enough to allow the use of steel dies
('warm pressing') also enables high pressures to be employed. The
method can also be combined with isostatic pressing by the use of
flexible steel containers. Although until recently hot pressing was
a laboratory technique, not well suited to production, it has been
developed to a semi-continuous stage for the production of a series
of oxide discs, and it has been reported to have been used on a small
scale for the continuous pressing of ferrites. It is particularly
suited to making simple cylindrical shapes to close dimensional
tolerances, but more complex shapes can be made, e.g. rocket
nozzles in silicon carbide.

9.4.9 Flame spraying[15]

The spraying of metals by feeding a wire into a gun where the
metal is atomised by a hot flame and sprayed on to a surface, for
example zinc wire sprayed on to a glass or other non-metallic surface,
has been a commonplace for many years. Recently the method has

been modified to enable non-metals to be sprayed for a variety of purposes ranging from the electrical insulation of small electronic components to the thermal and erosion protection of artificial satellites. A variety of ceramic coatings are produced on metal surfaces in this way. Two methods are commercially available :—
(1) Ceramic powder is fed into a spray gun, burning oxy-coal gas, oxy-hydrogen or oxy-acetylene. (2) The "Rockide" process in which the ceramic is fed into the gun in rod form. The design of the gun and the fuel used are of prime importance, and various new types of fuel have been developed, including metal powder. One process, known as the "Plasma jet" process, enables temperatures of over 15,000°C. to be obtained. One problem is to achieve good ceramic-metal adhesion, and it is necessary that the ceramic shall be above its softening point when it reaches the metal surface. Coatings can be built up to a thickness of 0.2 in. and over, and it can be arranged that the ceramic coating may be removed intact from the metal surface to form accurately dimensioned thin ceramic articles, particularly hollow shapes. Such articles are porous, and require sintering to make them dense.

9.4.10 Pyrolytic deposition[16]

The deposition of carbon on to an insulating support ('substrate') consisting of a rod or tube of porcelain or other ceramic is a well-established method of making electrical resistors. The ceramic support is heated to red heat or somewhat higher in a stream of an unsaturated hydrocarbon, which is thereby pyrolytically decomposed with deposition of a strongly adherent film of carbon in the form of graphite. There is at present great interest in the extension of this principle to the deposition of very dense protective coatings of graphite and also of silicon carbide (by the pyrolysis of methyl trichlorosilane and other organosilicon compounds) on to articles of less dense graphite, for nuclear and rocket motor parts.

REFERENCES

1. L. van Vlack, "Physical Ceramics for Engineers". Addison-Wesley Publishing Co. Inc., Reading, Mass ; Palo Alto, London, 1964, Chapter 8.

2. *Ibid*, Chapter 9.
3. F. A. Hummel, *J. Amer. Ceram. Soc.*, **34**, 235, 1951.
4. J. D. Walton jr. and M. D. Owen, "Mechanical Properties of Engineering Ceramics". W. W. Kriegel and H. Palmour (Eds.), Interscience Publishers, New York/London, 1961, pp. 149—173.
5. H. Boyd, *Ceram. Age*, **78**,(5), 41, 1962.
6. E. C. Martin, *Ceramics*, **9**,(114), 16, 1958.
7. W. D. Kingery, "Ceramic Fabrication Processes" Technology Press of the Massachusetts Institute of Technology and John Wiley & Sons Inc., New York/London, 1960, pp. 70—73.
8. T. W. Penrice, "Special Ceramics". P. Popper (Ed.), Heywood & Co. Ltd., London, 1960, pp. 329—338.
9. B. E. Vasilou. *Trans. Brit. Ceram. Soc.*, **56**,(10), 516, 1957.
10. M. A. Strivens. *Bull. Amer. Ceram. Soc.*, **42**,(1), 13, 1963.
11. .G. N. Howatt, R. G. Breckenridge and J. M. Brownlow. *J. Amer. Ceram. Soc.*, **30**,(8), 237, 1947.
12. J. White, *Proc. Brit. Ceram. Soc.*, (3), 155, 1965.
13. P. Popper, *Trans. 7th Int. Ceram. Congr.*, 1960, p. 451.
14. T. Vasilos and R. M. Spriggs. *Proc. Brit. Ceram. Soc.*, (3), 195—221, 1965.
15. N. N. Ault and Y. M. Wheildon, "Modern Materials", **2**. H. H. Hausner (Ed.), Academic Press, New York/London, 1960, pp. 63—106.
16. P. Popper, "Special Ceramics, 1962", Academic Press, London/New York, 1963, pp. 137—150.

FURTHER READING

W. A. Archbold and E. J. D. Smith. Super-refractories. "Ceramics—A Symposium", pp. 536—591. A. T. Green and G. H. Stewart (Eds.). The British Ceramic Society, Stoke-on-Trent, 1953.

D. G. Brown and R. W. Tymczak, A. Review of High-Temperature Materials. *J. Brit. Ceram. Soc.*, **2**,(1), 83, 1965.

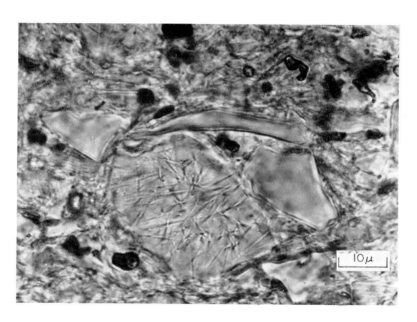

Plate I.—Photomicrograph of porcelain, deliberately over-fired, showing mullite crystals growing from the felspathic glass, undissolved quartz grains (note solution rims around these), and pores due to bloating.

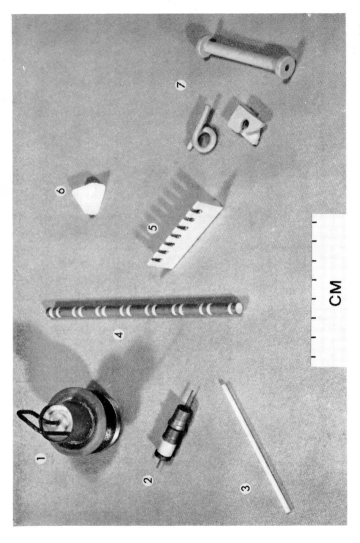

Plate II.—Alumina products. 1. Coupling loop for microwave valve (alumina sealed via Vacon 70 to a stainless steel welding flange) ; 2. Coaxial compression seal (valve terminal) ; 3. Thermocouple insulating tubing ; 4. Metallised connector rod ; 5. Metallised connector block ; 6. Triangular cutting tool insert ; 7. Textile guides. *(Courtesy of The Plessey Co. Ltd. and E.M.I. Ltd).*

CHAPTER 10

HIGH TEMPERATURE CERAMICS

II—OXIDES

10.1 Refractory oxides[1]

Among the many oxides useful in ceramics in one way or another, relatively few possess the combination of properties necessary for most of the high-temperature applications, namely have melting points above about 1500°C., are chemically stable and are at the same time commercially attractive. The more important ones are those of beryllium and magnesium in Group II ; aluminium in Group III ; silicon, zirconium and thorium in Group IV ; and unraium in Group VI. The sources of the more common oxides are referred to in Chapter 2.

10.2 Beryllia, BeO.
10.2.1 Source

Beryllium compounds are not abundant in nature, and are therefore more expensive than most ceramic materials. Beryllia is obtained from the mineral beryl, $3BeO.Al_2O_3.6SiO_2$, by chemical extraction, but since the physical properties have to be very carefully controlled in order to be able to sinter it to a high density, it is usual to start with the sulphate, hydroxide or other compound that will yield the oxide on calcination. The latter is a critical process, and controlled atmospheres appear to be necessary for the best results[2].

10.2.2 Properties and applications[3]

The more interesting properties, from a ceramic point of view, are :—

Melting point 2570°C.

Good chemical resistance—beryllia is one of the most stable oxides. It does, however, react with water vapour at high temperatures.

High electrical resistivity at high temperatures ($T_e > 1000°C$).

101

High mechanical strength.

Exceptionally high thermal conductivity, comparable to that of metals, and actually higher than that of beryllium metal.

Very good thermal shock resistance, mainly due to its high thermal conductivity. Both properties, however, tend to fall off rather rapidly at high temperatures.

A property of special interest in nuclear reactors is the ability to slow down neutrons efficiently without absorbing them, i.e. a low "neutron cross section".

As the position of beryllium in the Periodic Table would indicate, beryllium oxide bears some resemblance to alumina and to magnesia, but unlike these oxides it is poisonous. This fact was only realised long after it had been freely used as a constituent of fluorescent powders for vapour discharge lamps ; the toxic effects, which appear to depend to some extent on personal idiosyncracy, were not manifested until after a lapse of several years after the material had been handled. This, together with its comparatively high price, greatly hampered the development of its use until recently, when interest has revived, mainly because of its suitability for nuclear and special electronic applications. For these special applications the expense of providing the necessary health safeguards, such as high-velocity dust extraction hoods or totally enclosed glove boxes are evidently considered to be justified (The U.S. Atomic Energy Commission specifies an upper limit of beryllium oxide concentration of $2\mu g$ per m^3 of air). Work is now proceeding on its application to high power radio valves, to moderators for nuclear reactors, and to transistor 'heat sinks' which make use of its high thermal conductivity.

10.3 Magnesia, MgO

10.3.1 Properties

The sources of magnesia have already been mentioned (2.6). The properties of the chemically pure oxide are as follows :—

Melting point 2800°C.

Poor mechanical strength except in single crystal form.

High thermal expansion—highest of any oxide, and comparable to metals.

Poor thermal shock resistance.

Excellent electrical resistivity at high temperatures ($T_e > 1000°C.$).

High chemical resistance to metals and basic slags, but susceptible to re-hydration unless "dead-burnt".

10.3.2 Applications

The main use of magnesia in ceramics is of course as a steelworks and cement works refractory, but it is widely used in granular or pellet form for the fireproof insulation of cables, particularly ships' cables, and was patented some 20 years ago for this purpose under the name "Pyrotenax". It is used in a similar way for insulating the heater elements of domestic electric hot-plates and in numerous other types of equipment. Magnesium oxide is also produced in the form of thin discs, which consist of single crystals and are transparent to infra-red radiation. More recently polycrystalline transparent discs have been made by hot-pressing magnesium oxide with a small additive of lithium fluoride which provides some liquid phase to aid sintering.

10.4 Alumina, Al_2O_3

10.4.1 Properties

Owing to its abundance and its numerous attractive properties, alumina has become, in recent years, the most important electro-ceramic material after porcelain.

The melting point of pure alumina is 2040°C.

The mechanical strength of high-alumina ceramics, i.e. those containing more than, say 80% of Al_2O_3, is two or three times that of porcelain.

Alumina ceramics have comparatively high thermal shock resistance, due to mainly their high strength and fairly high thermal conductivity. The thermal expansion coefficient, on the other hand. is also rather high—about $8 \times 10^{-6}/°C$.

Alumina is chemically very stable.

In the corundum form, alumina is a very hard, abrasion-resistant material, although not so hard as silicon carbide.

Electrical characteristics, particularly resistivity and power factor, are good both at normal and at high temperatures. (Table 10.1 shows typical properties of high-alumina ceramics).

TABLE 10.1

Typical properties of high-alumina ceramics

Property	Units	90% Al_2O_3	95% Al_2O_3	99% Al_2O_3
Bulk density	g/cc	3.5	3.7	3.9
Modulus of rupture	lb in^2 ($\times 10^3$)	30	50	80
Modulus of elasticity	lb in^2 ($\times 10^7$)	3	4.5	6
Softening temperature	°C.	1600	1750	1900
Coefficient of linear thermal expansion (20—500°C)	°C^{-1} ($\times 10^{-6}$)	6.5	7.0	7.5
Thermal conductivity	cal °C^{-1}cm^{-1} sec^{-1}	0.02	0.035	0.05
T_e	°C.	700	850	950
Permittivity (1 Mc/s)	—	8.1	9.0	9.5
Power factor (1 Mc/s)	— ($\times 10^{-4}$)	4	3	2

10.4.2 High-alumina compositions[4]

Many products are made from compositions containing between 80 and 95% of Al_2O_3. A typical high quality material would contain 90—95% Al_2O_3, up to 4% of bentonite or very plastic clay to aid shaping and lower the sintering temperature, about 1% of magnesium oxide to restrain crystal growth, and possibly a few other small additions such as calcium oxide. Because of their effect on refractoriness, chemical resistance and electrical properties, the impurities present in the starting material (particularly soda and silica) must be low in amount and be carefully controlled.

In all except the purest alumina, some liquid phase is present during sintering, but in alumina containing over 99% Al_2O_3, it may be completely absent, although it is not easy to be quite certain that this is so in particular cases. Sintering temperatures of commercial high-aluminas range from about 1550 to 1650°C., but may be up to 1800°C. for pure, e.g. "recrystallised", aluminas, unless hot pressing is used.

10.4.3 Electrical and electronic applications

Many different kinds of electrical insulators are made in high-alumina, particularly in tubular form, varying from thermocouple one- to four-bore tubes only a few mm. in diameter to large furnace muffles. Small diameter tubes are made by extrusion, but larger tubes are usually slip cast. Some fairly simple shapes of insulator may be dry pressed.

The largest output of alumina ceramics is accounted for by *sparking plug insulators*[5]. These are produced on an increasingly great scale—of the order of a million per week in this country alone. In the early days of the internal combustion engine insulators were of porcelain, but this was superseded by compositions in the MgO-Al_2O_3-SiO_2 system, sillimanite, mullite, mica, etc., in order to achieve the necessary thermal shock resistance. Then, in the 1920's, as service conditions were becoming more severe, mullite and zircon became the chief materials. Pure alumina insulators were introduced in Germany in the early 1930's, under the name "Sinterkorund". Owing to the absence of fluxes the firing temperature had to be around 1750°C., but later developments showed that a small amount of non-alkaline fluxes could be tolerated, so enabling firing temperatures to be substantially reduced. In a modern internal combustion engine temperatures up to 850°C. and pressures up to 900 lb./in.^{2} may occur in extreme conditions ; the insulator must withstand these and the rapid fluctuations between conditions during the low temperature and pressure induction stroke and the high temperature and pressure conditions at ignition. Also voltages up to 12,000 must be withstood, as well as the high mechanical stresses applied during the making of the metal-to-metal gas-tight joints. Further, the use of lead-containing anti-knock fuels necessitates keeping the SiO_2 content low, to avoid fluxing with the PbO. The fairly good thermal conductivity of alumina enables the heat to be conducted away from the hot end of the plug more easily than with other materials, so that longer, hotter-running tips can be used; this helps to burn off any carbon deposited. A 95% alumina is normally used. The following details are merely typical, and there are numerous variations depending upon particular applications and manufacturers. In order to facilitate milling down to the required fineness (around 3 microns average diameter), alumina hydrate is milled to a controlled fineness before calcining, then remilled for a short time to break up aggregates. After screening, this material is wet-mixed with the rest of the ingredients, including a wax emulsion or other binder. The screened and magnetted slip is spray dried and isostatically pressed into blanks having the approximate external profile, a mandrel introduced axially into the material before pressing providing the bore in the insulator blank. The final external shaping is done by form grinding, using a grinding wheel into which the required shape has been impressed by crushing with a hardened steel piece ; alternatively profile turning may be used. The insulators are fired in tunnel kilns at around 1600°C. and then glazed, usually with a low solubility lead glaze. The steel centre pin and bottom electrode are assembled, electrical connection between them being made by pressing the ends inside the insulator into a mixture of copper powder and glass which is then heated to soften it. The complete insulator is mechanically sealed into its steel shell with a washer and sealing ring, so that the whole assembly is gas tight (see Fig. 10.1). A high voltage flashover test is applied to every insulator as a check on its soundness.

Microwave valve parts are another important application of alumina ceramics. In the generation of very high frequency radio power, valves are required to operate at temperatures up to 600°C.

Fig. 10.1.—Spark plug construction. (*Courtesy of A.C. Delco Division of General Motors Ltd.*).

or more, and the glass envelope has to be replaced by either a ceramic "window" in the form of a disc inserted into a metal envelope or a cylinder sealed to metal end pieces ; these are for the purpose of allowing the radiation to pass through to the outside. Ceramics are also required for other parts of valves, and in fact two types of material are called for : one a high grade material suitable for valve body parts, and the other a special grade suitable for high-power microwave windows, and normally consisting of alumina containing over 96% Al_2O_3, although there is now some interest in beryllia for this purpose. Both types of material must be vacuum-tight to a high standard, have high mechanical strength, high thermal conductivity (both from the point of view of thermal shock resistance and to avoid excessive temperature rise), conform to a close electrical specification, be capable of being metallised, be stable under a variety of processing and operating conditions, and in the case of windows the material must be free of voids or inclusions which might interfere with the passage of radiation.

A variety of sizes are required, mainly in the form of tubes or discs, with diameters ranging from a fraction of an inch up to a foot or so. Disc type windows are sealed around their circumference into a sleeve of metal of matched thermal expansion, e.g. Kovar. Tolerances on thickness have to be down to 0.001 in. and on a typical diameter of 3—4 in. similar tolerances are necessary to produce vacuum-tight seals. Machining after firing is necessary in order to achieve these tolerances and to produce a fine surface finish suitable for metallizing and sealing.

Other electronic applications of alumina include many small insulators, capacitor dielectrics and printed circuit substrates (bases).

10.4.4 Chemical applications

The cracking of petroleum involves the use of catalysts which are carried by ceramic supports which may be either coated or impregnated with the catalyst. Although other materials than alumina are used for this purpose, alumina has the advantages of good thermal conductivity (highly exothermic reactions occur in the fluid bed converters used), chemical inertness, high abrasion resistance and high mechanical strength. Supports are made in spherical form, or as pellets or rings, up to an inch or so in diameter. Those intended for coating are of medium porosity, with a rough exterior ; those for impregnation have a high porosity, with an open network of pores.

Alumina is also used for numerous other chemical and metallurgical purposes where special chemical resistance is necessary, particularly crucibles.

10.4.5 Mechanical applications

Cutting tools[6]—Prior to 1930 porcelain had been used to cut comparatively soft metals at low speeds, but the development of tool steels, and later of cemented carbide cutting tools consisting of tungsten carbide bonded with cobalt, diverted interest from purely ceramic cutting tools until the latter part of the second world war, when the use of alumina began to be investigated because of the shortage of tungsten. Other possible materials harder than alumina are diamond, boron carbide and silicon carbide; but diamond is too expensive, and the last two are too brittle, so that the choice fell on alumina. However, the quality of alumina ceramics available at that time was not good enough, being inferior to cemented carbide, and little progress was made until the 1950's, when further work was stimulated by the demand for higher machining speeds for automated processes. Tool tips made from 95% Al_2O_3 compositions had some success, but still suffered from brittleness and rapid wear, although they were a great improvement on porcelain. But it was only when fine-grained, substantially glass-free compositions containing 98—99% Al_2O_3 were fabricated by hot pressing (at about 1200°C.) that ceramic tool tips became a commercial proposition. Owing to what is otherwise an advantage of alumina—its chemical stability—it was found impracticable to weld alumina to a steel shank, and ceramic tools are therefore made in the form of inserts clamped into suitably shaped steel jaws, and are simply removed when worn. Various shapes are produced : square, triangular, etc., to give several cutting edges which can be successively indexed. Tools can be reground by the use of a diamond wheel. In addition to turning tools, milling cutters can be ceramic-tipped, and other machining processes can also be used. Various metals and other materials can be machined, and particular success has been achieved in machining cast iron and graphite. Cutting speeds are up to 1500 surface ft./min., depths of cut up to more than $\frac{1}{2}$ in., and feed rates up to 6 in./min. or more. The use of alumina cutting tools not only allows more rapid machining, but gives longer production runs, lower tool costs and improved finishes. Other advantages are that no coolants are required, and that there is no tendency to weld to metals. On the other hand their toughness, tensile strength and thermal shock resistance are not so high as some alternative materials, and the number of applications for which they can replace materials such as cemented carbides appears to be limited at present.

Abrasives—Corundum has long been used in powder form as an abrasive, e.g. emery, for grinding and polishing, and for making abrasive wheels (see also Section 12.5).

Textile guides—The tremendous growth in the manufacture of man-made fibres, some of which are very abrasive, particularly when loaded with certain oxides, has resulted in a demand for textile guides which would be much more abrasion-resistant, in order to avoid the frequent replacement necessary when using conventional ceramics like porcelain. High-alumina ceramics, of similar quality to sparking plug insulators, have proved very successful, in spite of their higher initial cost, which is more than compensated by increased life. Many different shapes are made : tubes, eyelets, rollers, "pigtails", and other more complicated shapes which are sometimes fabricated by injection moulding. Close tolerances are demanded in some cases, and have to be obtained by machining after sintering ; also surfaces often have to be ground and sometimes polished to give specified finishes to minimise friction.

Other mechanical applications of alumina include : high temperature bearings ; pump parts such as liners and plungers ; dies for the cold drawing of metal tubes, bars and wires ; sprayed protective coatings on metals for turbo-jet engines and rockets. In the form of single crystals, alumina is used for bearings in clocks, meters and other precision instruments. These crystals are made by the Verneuil method, in which alumina powder is fused in an oxy-hydrogen flame and allowed to fall on to a refractory plate, where it builds up into a "boule" consisting of a single crystal. More recently single crystals of alumina with small additions of other metals have been used as laser elements, particularly rubies, in which the additive is chromium.

A recent application of alumina is for producing the nose

cones ("radomes") of rockets. These may be of the order of 6 in. in diameter and 18 in. high, or considerably larger, and a fraction of an inch in wall thickness ; the latter has to be made to a tolerance of 0.001 in. in order not to interfere with the passage of microwave radiation. Possible methods of shaping include flame spraying using a steel or graphite former ; and slip casting or slip spraying on to a steel former, followed by isostatic pressing. After a preliminary firing the radomes are machined on a lathe, using diamond tools, and finally fired. In addition to being mechanically strong and resistant to thermal shock, the product is very resistant to erosion by rain. In nuclear technology alumina is used in the form of spacers, supports for fuel elements and for various other structural components. For thermal insulation, alumina is used as a loose-fill powder and also as bubble alumina, which is blown from fused alumina and which is an excellent high-temperature light-weight insulator, with a bulk density of only 1.3 g/cc.

A typical selection of alumina piece parts is shown on Plate II (facing page 101).

10.5 Fused silica, SiO_2

In spite of the fundamental importance of crystalline and cryptocrystalline forms of silica in many ceramics, the inclusion of fused silica as a ceramic may be questioned, since glass-working techniques are used in the manufacture of this type of ware. However, its technical importance is such that it should not be excluded from a consideration of refractory single oxides. It has long been used for laboratory and chemical ware, electric furnace muffles, etc.

Its melting point is 1710°C., but the upper limit of temperature for continuous operation is about 1200°C., above which it begins to devitrify rather rapidly to cristobalite. The other important properties are :—

Excellent high temperature electrical resistivity.

Excellent thermal shock resistance, due mainly to an exceptionally low coefficient of thermal expansion (0.55 × 10^{-6}/°C. between room temperature and 500°C.).

Complete resistance to attack by acids other than hydrofluoric acid.

Recently there has been some interest in slip casting of fused silica for rocketry applications, including radomes[7].

10.6 Zirconia, ZrO_2

Interest in zirconia for electroceramics is due mainly to its refractoriness (m.p. 2700°C.) and its chemical resistance, although the fact that is becomes electrically semi-conducting at red heat has led to a limited use as a muffle which forms its own heating element at high temperatures. For use as kiln furniture it has to be stabilised against a monoclinic-tetragonal crystal change at about 1000°C., accompanied by a 9% volume change, which would otherwise be destructive. This is achieved by the addition of a few per cent of lime or rare earth oxides. Zirconium oxide can be sintered rapidly by hot pressing above 1000°C. It is about the only placing material with which ceramics based on barium titanate will not react, and is used as a powder as well as stabilised zirconia plates. It is also used as an additive in a number of special electroceramic compositions, and is one of the main constituents of certain piezoelectric ceramics. CaO-doped ZrO_2 is being studied as a solid-state electrolyte, e.g. for fuel cells.

10.7 Thorium oxide, ThO_2

This occurs only in small amounts, in a number of minerals, as the silicate, sometimes in association with zircon as in monazite sand. It has the highest melting point of any oxide, 3300°C., the temperature of the hottest part of an oxyacetylene flame. It is also chemically the most stable oxide known, e.g. to molten metals, and for this reason it is used for making metallurgical crucibles. One interesting property is its high light emissivity, which is made use of in incandescent gas mantles. For this purpose a small percentage of cerium oxide is added to "activate" the light emission. Small amounts of impurities cause ThO_2 to become semi-conducting. When irradiated with neutrons it becomes transmuted to uranium 233, a fissionable isotope, and it is therefore a possible source of nuclear power.

10.8 Uranium oxide, UO_2

The main interest in uranium compounds is of course their potentional and actual use as the fissionable material in nuclear devices. The high melting point of the oxide—2800°C.—makes it attractive for use at higher temperatures than the metal. UO_2 readily takes up oxygen up to the formula $UO_{2.20}$ The material containing excess oxygen, particularly $UO_{2.17}$, gives higher sintered densities than the stoichiometric compound, and for this reason hot pressing in graphite dies, with consequent reduction, does not always yield the highest density. If fired in an oxidising atmosphere UO_2 tends to become U_3O_8.

An interesting example of the application of a metallurgical technique to ceramics is the use of *swaging* to compact uranium oxide in the manufacture of nuclear fuel elements[8]. This process, used for many years to reduce the diameter of billets of brittle metals like tungsten, and more recently of uranium metal, consists of passing the billet through a machine where it is subjected to a series of rapid hammer-like blows which reduce the diameter without altering the shape of the cross-section. In one method used for the manufacture of fuel rods, UO_2 is converted to the nitrate, which is calcined to give UO_3, and this is then reduced in hydrogen to the lower oxide. After sintering, crushing and grading, the oxide, now in granular form, is filled into a thin-walled, cylindrical metal container. Pre-compaction is carried out by vibratory compaction (see Section 5.2.6) up to 90% of the theoretical density, and the cross section of the container is then reduced by swaging (one or more passes through the machine may be required).

REFERENCES

1. E. Ryshkewitch, "Oxide Ceramics". Academic Press, New York/London, 1960.

2. C. Hyde, J. F. Quirk and W. H. Duckworth, *Ceramics*, **10**, (120), 10, 1959.

3. P. G. Taylor and I. J. Holland, *Eng. Materials Design*, **5**,(9), 646, 1962.

4. D. W. Luks, "Electronic and Newer Ceramics". J. J. Svec, G. L. Vincent and K. A. Brent (Eds.), Industrial Publications Inc., Chicago, 1960, Chaps. 14, 15 and 16.

5. G. C. Martin, *Ceramics*, **9,** (114), 12, 1958.

6. W. M. Wheildon, "Modern Materials", **2.** H. H. Hausner (Ed.), Academic Press, New York/London, 1960.

7. J. D. Fleming, *Bull. Amer. Ceram. Soc.*, **40,**(12), 748, 1961.

8. J. E. Brown, *Ceram. Age*, **75,** (1), 20, 1960.

CHAPTER 11

HIGH TEMPERATURE CERAMICS

III—NON-OXIDES, CERMETS

11.1 Non-oxides—general[1]

The intensive search in recent years for refractories with particular combinations of properties led naturally to the field of non-oxides, which contains some of the most refractory materials known. As well as stimulating a study of new compositions substantial improvements have been made in the quality of well-known materials such as silicon carbide.

The only refractory non-metallic element of practical importance in this context is carbon. Although boron and silicon have high melting points—2300 and 1420°C. respectively—they are not chemically stable at high temperatures, and oxidise readily.

Binary compounds of most interest are certain non-metallic ones in which one of the pair is an element of Groups IVB to VIIB. Some refractory compounds of metals and non-oxides are described as "hard metals", and in fact we are in one of the borderlands betweens metals and ceramics. A broad line may be drawn between materials in which a certain amount of non-oxide dissolves in a metal, e.g. carbon in iron, which are undoubtedly metallic, and those that consist substantially of a compound of the two, the metal atoms not being bonded to one another, and which are regarded as ceramics.

One point of difference between oxides and non-oxides is that in oxides, in which the bonding is predominantly ionic, the oxygens, being comparatively large, form the framework of the structure, with the cations occupying the space inside ; whilst in many non-oxides, in which the bonding is predominantly covalent—particularly nitrides, carbides and borides—it is the more electropositive elements which form the framework, with the more electronegative elements occupying the intervening spaces because of their comparatively small atomic radii. (The *atomic* radius of nitrogen is 0.17Å, compared

113

with the *ionic* radius of oxygen, 1.32Å). In these interstitial compounds, which have some metallic characteristics, such as low electrical resistivity, it is not necessary for all the interstices to be filled, so that the compositions are frequently non-stoichometric.

11.2 Carbon

11.2.1 Source, structure, properties

Commercial sources of carbon include charcoal, coal, gas carbon, mineral oils, natural graphite, and foundry coke. There are various types of amorphous carbon and two crystalline forms : graphite and diamond. All types, except diamond, are electrical conductors. Carbon sublimes at 3925°C., but it begins to oxidise at temperatures well below red heat, this being its main disadvantage except where reducing conditions are required. When heated to moderately high temperatures amorphous carbon is converted to graphite, with an increase in thermal and electrical conductivity. *Graphite*[2] has a hexagonal layer structure, with only weak bonds between the layers (cf. kaolinite, talc, mica), which accounts for its lubricating properties. The crystals are highly anisotropic. For example the thermal conductivity is 0.006 and 0.6 cgs units respectively, at right angles and parallel to the main crystal plane ; the corresponding figures for electrical conductivity are 4×10^3 and 4×10^5 ohm^{-1}cm^{-1}. One unusual characteristic of graphite is an increase of mechanical strength with increasing temperature, due to a certain amount of reorientation, with a decrease in anisotropy. Because some of the electrons within the plane are relatively free to move, graphite behaves in many ways as a metal when the properties are measured parallel to the planes.

11.2.2 Products

The many applications of carbon include : refractories for glass shaping, crucibles for metallurgy, heat exchangers, filters, various chemical ware, directly heated electric muffles, dies for hot pressing, commutator brushes and other electrical contacts, resistors, and moderators for nuclear reactors.

Porous ware is made from coke, bonded with tar or pitch. This is moulded hot, allowed to set, and fired to carbonise the bond. The product may be converted into graphite by further high temperature treatment, e.g. at 2500 to 3000°C. Both carbon and graphite products can be made impervious by impregnating with resins.

Vitreous ware is made by carefully grading finely ground coke and bonding with clay, felspar, etc. ; other additions include silicon carbide to give increased strength and refractoriness. The fired material has a higher refractoriness than clay itself, apparently due to the formation of a rigid carbon framework. Graphite crucibles have the advantage of high thermal conductivity, which saves time in heating, good mechanical strength, toughness, out-standing shock resistance, and of not tending to oxidise the contents. Naturally-occuring graphite flakes are particularly suitable for making crucibles. Graphite products for other applications are made by extrusion and turning, and by pressing. Extruded ware shows crystal orientation effects such as electrical and thermal anisotropy. Since the advent of nuclear energy graphite has been an important moderator material[3], and some 80,000 tons of high purity material has been used for this purpose in the United States, Great Britain and France alone during the last 20 years. More recently it has been used as a container for uranium carbide fuel elements, e.g. in the "Dragon" reactor on Winfrith Heath. Mention has already been made of pyrolytically deposited graphite (Section 9.4.10).

11.3 Borides[4]

Borides are mainly metallic in nature, having high electrical and thermal conductivity. They are very hard, brittle, and have rather poor oxidation resistance. The borides of the fourth, fifth and sixth groups of the Periodic Table are fairly well known, particularly those of titanium, zirconium, chromium and molybdenum, the melting points of the first two being among the highest known—2920 and 3050°C. respectively ; the last two have high mechanical strength and hardness at elevated temperatures, cermets based on chromium boride having the greatest high temperature strength of any known material—100,000 lb./in.^{2} at 1550°C.

There are various methods of making borides, two common processes being : (*a*) by the direct combination of boron with a metal or metal hydride—a somewhat expensive method, but useful for making high purity products for research ; (*b*) by the reaction of boron with a metal oxide, in the presence of sufficient carbon or boron carbide to reduce the metal oxide.

Fabrication is by hot pressing the powder at 1400 to 1650°C., or by cold pressing followed by sintering in an inert or reducing atmosphere, e.g. hydrogen. Borides have also been flame sprayed using a plasma jet.

The applications of borides include : zirconium boride thermo-couple sheaths for use in liquid iron and steel ; titanium and zirconium borides as rocket nozzles ; chromium boride with nickel as a low temperature brazing alloy for nickel ; various electrical devices such as contact materials, resistors, thermionic emitters, semi-conductors ; and some nuclear uses.

11.4 Carbides

11.4.1 General

Carbides are among the most refractory materials known, but like the borides, are not very resistant to oxidation at high tem-peratures. They are all electrically conducting, except those of the alkali and alkaline earth metals, but both these are decomposed by water. The carbides of practical importance are confined to Groups III, IV, V and VI. The usual method of making carbides is by the high temperature reaction of the elements or of carbon with the oxide of the other element.

11.4.2 Boron carbide, B_4C

This has a melting point of 2350°C. and is the best known of the Group III carbides because of its extreme hardness, which approaches that of diamond and has led to its use in wear-resistant nozzles, gauges, and other applications requiring high abrasion resistance. It can be hot pressed to give a self-bonded product of up to 99% theoretical density. It is also used for lapping and polishing hard metals, e.g. for wire drawing dies and in the form of a dressing stick for dressing grinding wheels. Another property of interest is its high neutron cross section, i.e. its ability to absorb neutrons, and it is therefore used, in conjuction with graphite, for control rods and shields in nuclear reactors. Boron carbide is made by the reaction of boric oxide with petroleum coke in an arc furnace at 2600°C., the product being ground in steel mills, then washed with acetone and dried.

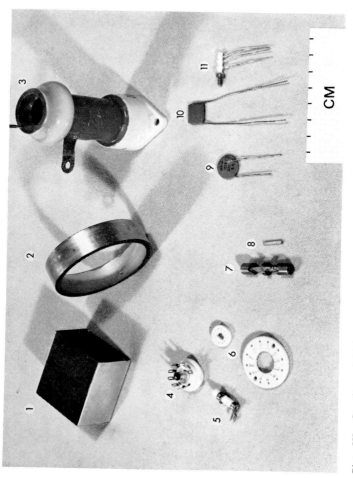

Plate III.—Steatite and high-permittivity products. 1. Ultrasonic generator block ; 2. Ultrasonic generator ring ; 3. Transmitter capacitor (mounted in steatite base) ; 4. Steatite valve base (metal parts fitted) ; 5. Steatite bush seal ; 6. Steatite valve bases ; 7. Accelerometer unit ; 8. Bimorph for gramophone pick-up ; 9. Disc capacitor ; 10. Stacked film capacitor ; 11. Tubular capacitor. (*Courtesy of The Plessey Co. Ltd. and The United Insulation Co. Ltd.*).

CM

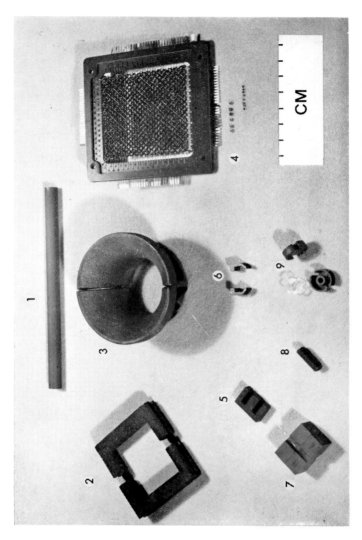

Plate IV.—Ferrite products. 1. Aerial rod ; 2. Pair of U-cores ; 3. Line scan television yoke ; 4. Memory core matrix and individual cores ; 5. E-core ; 6. Pieces for tape recorder reading head ; 7. Permanent magnet pole pieces ; 8. Screw-core ; 9. Pair of pot-core pieces with plastic bobbin.
(*Courtesy of The Plessey Co. Ltd.*).

11.4.3 Silicon carbide, SiC

This material decomposes without melting at 2700°C. It is now over 65 years since it began to be used industrially as an abrasive, and clay-bonded products such as kiln furniture and electric heating elements have long been familiar. Silicon carbide exists in several crystalline forms, the commercial product being the α-form. The properties that have led to its widespread use are its hardness, electrical conductivity, and excellent thermal shock resistance, the last being due to high mechanical strength, moderately low thermal expansion and high thermal conductivity. In an oxidising atmosphere the formation of a thin adherent film of silica protects it to a large extent from further oxidation; the maximum temperature for continuous use is 1500—1600°C., and some 600°C. higher in an inert atmosphere.

The method of manufacture is by heating a mixture of coke, sand and salt in a resistance furnace, using coke as the heating element, at 2200°C.

More recently, *self-bonded* silicon carbide has been introduced[5]. This is made by pressing various grades of silicon carbide powder mixed with graphite, followed by reaction sintering the compact in silicon vapour. The product can be made into quite intricate shapes, which can be finished to give close dimensional tolerances by diamond grinding. The material is impermeable with superior properties to the clay-bonded product ; for example it maintains a bending strength of 28,000 lb./in.[2] from room temperature up to 1400°C. Hot pressed silicon carbide is also made. In the form of cellular lightweight foam, silicon carbide can be used for thermal insulation up to 2200°C. Colourless 'grains' (crystals) of silicon carbide are now available, of high purity, which are stable at high temperatures and have semi-conductor properties of potential use in high temperature transistor applications. A related application arises from the fact that when a very high voltage is applied to silicon carbide its resistance falls sharply. This is made use of in voltage surge arresters, e.g. lightning arresters, which absorb the high current which otherwise would be liable to cause damage. The non-linear relationship between current and voltage is also used to balance the strengths of telephone signals by partially short-circuiting the stronger ones. Pyrolytic coatings of silicon carbide on graphite are now being used for improving the oxidation resistance of the latter for nuclear and rocket motor applications. Much work is also being carried out to produce single crystals of silicon carbide from the vapour phase for semi-conductor applications.

11.4.3 Titanium carbide, TiC

A suggestion was made as long ago as 1920 to use titanium carbide as an abrasive, and it was produced commercially in 1938 by the reaction of titanium oxide and carbon in an arc furnace. Later an improved product was obtained by the addition of metallic iron to the mix, giving a pure, completely crystalline product. This method has also been adapted to the production of a number of other carbides. Titanium carbide, which has a melting point of 3150°C., forms the basis of a series of commercially successful cermets, and it is also available in both hot pressed and powder forms.

11.4.4 Zirconium carbide, ZrC

This has been used as a coating on uranium oxide particles for nuclear reactors, being 'vapour plated', i.e. pyrolytically deposited, from a mixture of zirconium tetrachloride and methane, with hydrogen as a carrier gas, at about 1500°C. The melting point of zirconium carbide is 3530°C.

11.4.5 Hafnium carbide, HfC

This compound is interesting as having the highest melting point of any known material—3890°C. It has a limited application as a nuclear control material owing to its high neutron cross section.

11.4.6 Tungsten carbide, WC

This forms the basis of the now familiar 'cemented carbide' cutting tools and tool inserts. It has a melting point of 2600°C. The method of preparation is by heating a mixture of the metal with carbon black at 1600°C. in a graphite container. After cooling in hydrogen the product is wet milled in carbide mills.

11.4.7 Uranium carbide, UC

There is also a dicarbide, UC_2, which is of somewhat less interest, but the monocarbide, UC, melting point 2300°C., is an important nuclear fuel for high temperature reactors. It is prepared by the carbon reduction of uranium oxide. The powder so prepared is pyrophoric when the grain size is less than about 40 microns. It can be compacted into rods and then sintered, or a mixture of uranium metal powder and graphite can be hot pressed at 1000—1100°C. In conjuction with thorium carbide, uranium carbide is prepared in the form of spheroids by melting. As the mixed carbide hydrolyses on exposure to air, the material requires a protective coating, e.g. of carbon. Fabrication of uranium carbide products has to be carried out in an inert atmosphere, e.g. argon, because of their reactivity.

11.5 Silicides

Molybdenum disilicide, $MoSi_2$, melting point 1870°C., is now established commercially in the form of electric furnace elements (Kanthal 'Super') for operation up to 1700°C.[6]. Its more out-standing properties are its metallic-type electrical conductivity and its oxidation resistance ; the latter has led to its use as a protective coating on silicon carbide elements. For many purposes its resist-ivity at room temperature is rather low, and attempts have been made to increase it by compounding it with alumina.

Various other silicides are of possible commercial interest, for example those of chromium and titanium. In general, silicides have excellent thermal shock resistance, low electrical resistivity, and are hard and brittle at room temperature.

11.6 Nitrides
11.6.1 General

Although brittle, hard and not very resistant to oxidation at high temperatures, many nitrides are non-metallic in character, and are very good electrical insulators, even at high temperatures, in contrast to the non-oxides described so far.

11.6.2 Boron nitride, BN[7]

There has been much interest in recent times in this material, which exists in two sharply contrasting crystalline forms : (*1*) 'White graphite', which has a platey hexagonal structure resembling graphite ; in fact it may be regarded as derived from the latter by the substitution of alternate boron and nitrogen atoms for carbon in the lattice. Unlike graphite, however, it is an excellent electrical insulator. It resembles graphite in being very soft, and having a low coefficient of friction ; (2) 'Borazon', which has a cubic structure resembling diamond, is extremely hard, and is formed when white graphite is heated at high temperature and pressure. It is the hexagonal form which is of most interest at the present time, although it can scarcely be called a new material, as it was known as long ago as 1842 (Balmain). It sublimes at high temperature, but has been melted under pressure at 3000°C.

It is prepared by the reaction of boric oxide or boron chloride with ammonia. One method is to make compacts of boric oxide containing some calcium phosphate as a filler to prevent the former fusing together into an impermeable mass during the subsequent reaction. The compacts are shredded and nitrided by treating with ammonia at 900°C. ($B_2O_3 + 2NH_3 \rightarrow 2BN + 3H_2O$). The product is ground, and the calcium phosphate extracted with acid ; after washing and drying, the material is extracted with alcohol to remove residual boric acid. Articles can be fabricated by hot pressing at temperatures up to about 1900°C.

Boron nitride may also be prepared using other reactions, e.g. that of boron trichloride with ammonia at 1600°C. The product of this reaction, when in powder form, is an excellent thermal insulator because of its low bulk density ($\sim$0.1 g/cm.^{3}).

The mechanical strength of boron nitride in ceramic form is not very high, and resistance to attack by water and alcohol is not very good, but boron nitride has some important advantages : namely it is machinable after sintering, has a low coefficient of friction, a low power factor, and a high electrical resistivity (T_e 950—1350°C.). Possible uses include various electronic valve insulators, nuclear and rocket parts. Uses for the material in powder form have also been suggested, one arising from its low thermal conductivity is thermal insulation in high-frequency induction vacuum furnaces.

11.6.3 Silicon nitride, Si_3N_4 [8]

This is a comparatively recently prepared material, discovered during a search for high temperature materials for turbine blades. It sublimes above 1900°C. It is produced in two forms : porous and dense. The former is made by reaction sintering silicon compacts of the desired shape in nitrogen at temperatures above 1200°C. The nitrogen diffuses into the compact and forms a mass of silicon nitride crystals. Although in this form it does not approach the dense form in properties, its mechanical strength is quite high and its thermal shock resistance is outstanding. Although porous, if glazed it can be used for electrical applications. To make the dense form it is necessary to use hot pressing and to machine after firing, which add considerably to the cost of production if high dimensional accuracy is required. However, this is justified for certain applications as it is the strongest of all ceramic materials, with a bending strength of up to 100,000 lb./in.^{2}, and this, with its lightness, gives it a strength to density ratio equal to that of steel, particularly at high temperatures, its bending strength at 1200°C. being still 50,000 —70,000 lb./in^2. It has a high thermal conductivity, low expansion and the best thermal shock resistance of any known ceramic except graphite. It is as hard as sapphire, is comparatively resistant to oxidation, abrasion, attack by molten metals, and to high temperature creep. The only important respect in which it is inferior to metals is in having the brittleness common to all ceramics. In addition to its application to turbine blades, silicon nitride has been used or suggested for rocket nozzles, pumps, mechanical valves, crucibles and welding jigs.

11.6.4 Aluminium nitride, AlN [9]

This compound, which melts at 2450°C., has been known for many years, but was not used because of hydrolysis when exposed to a damp atmosphere. Recently it has been found that heating it to 2000°C. induces resistance to attack by water vapour. In one method of preparation aluminium powder is levitated in a radio-frequency field while being nitrided, which eliminates the need for an unreactive container. The strength of aluminium nitride in single crystal whisker form is enormous. Possible uses of aluminium nitride include containers for molten aluminium, and as a semi-conductor.

11.6.5 Uranium nitride, UN

Both the nitride and the carbonitride have recently been studied as potential nuclear fuel elements.

11.7 Sulphides

Because of the larger size of the sulphur ion compared with that of oxygen the bonding in sulphides is somewhat weaker, their melting points are lower, and their stability is less than in the case of the corresponding oxides. However, some are sufficiently refractory to be of practical interest. These include the sulphides of *zinc*, *cadmium* and *lead*, which in addition have useful photo-electric and luminescent properties, e.g. PbS for infra-red detection, Zn/CdS for luminescent lighting panels. Uranium and thorium monosulphides have been investigated as potential nuclear fuels.

11.8 Halides

Very few halides are of interest as high temperature materials because they are mostly soluble in water and are not very refractory, although a few have melting points of over 1000°C., e.g. *magnesium fluoride* (m.p. 1400°C.) and *calcium fluoride* (m.p. 1260°C.). The latter is resistant to attack by molten uranium metal, and is used for this purpose in the form of slip cast crucibles, which are fired at a fairly low temperature[10].

REFERENCES

1. P. Popper, "Progress in Dielectrics", **1**. General editor : J. B. Birks, Heywood & Co. Ltd., London, 1959, pp. 219—289.
2. L. C. F. Blackman, *Research*, **13**, 390, 441, 492, 1960.
3. W. H. Kohl, "Materials and Techniques for Electron Tubes". Reinhold Publishing Co., New York, and Chapman & Hall Ltd., London, 1960, Chap. 4.
4. B. Aronson, "Modern Materials", **2**. H. H. Hausner (Ed.), Academic Press, New York/London, 1960, pp. 143—224.
5. P. Popper, "Special Ceramics". P. Popper (Ed.), Heywood & Co., London, 1960, pp. 209—219.
6. J. Haglund, *Interceram*, No. 7, 52, 1958.
7. T. A. Ingles and P. Popper, as Ref. 5 above, p. 144.
8. P. Popper and S. N. Ruddlesden, *Trans. Brit. Ceram. Soc.*, **60**, 603, 1961.
9. C. F. Cooper, C. M. George and W. J. Hopkins, *Research*, **13**, 49, 1960.
10. P. Rado, as Ref. 5 above, p. 237.

CHAPTER 12

HIGH TEMPERATURE CERAMICS

IV—VARIOUS PRODUCTS AND APPLICATIONS

12.1 Cermets[1]

At high temperatures ceramics have important advantages over metals in being more refractory, having greater creep resistance, greater chemical stability and greater abrasion resistance ; on the other hand metals have higher thermal conductivity and higher resistance to thermal and mechanical shock. Cermets represent an attempt to combine the more desirable characteristics of both classes of material in one product.

The general method of manufacture is to mill together a mixture of the ceramic and metal powders, and to cold press, isostatically press, hot press, or extrude the shapes required. Sintering is usually carried out in hydrogen or neutral atmospheres. The proportion of ceramic to metal varies greatly. One or both phases may be continuous, e.g. may consist of continuous filaments of the metallic component—an advantage where good thermal or electrical conductivity is required. *Infiltrated cermets*, having improved impact resistance, have been made by the infiltration of a porous skeleton of a refractory ceramic with a metal. Examples are titanium carbide with iron, nickel or cobalt, and alumina with silver. Graded cermets can be produced in this way, consisting substantially of metal on the surface, and changing to ceramic at the centre.

There are three main types of cermet compositions : (*i*) *oxide-based*, e.g. alumina-chromium ; (*ii*) *carbide-based*, e.g. tungsten carbide-cobalt, titanium carbide-nickel ; and (*iii*) *boride-*, *silicide-* and *nitride-based*.

(*i*) These have good high-temperature load-bearing strength and chemical stability, but the latter property creates a problem in manufacture, as it makes ceramic-to-metal bonding difficult. The original and most extensive study of alumina-metal cermets was made with Al_2O_3—Fe and Al_2O_3—Cr combinations, the objective being the development of a high-temperature, high-strength, thermal shock resistant material for jet propulsion devices such as flame holders and nozzles. Other products include thermocouple protection tubes, pouring spouts for molten copper, mechanical seals and thermocouple protection tubes for use in corrosive atmospheres. Sintering is carried out in hydrogen, some provision being made for a limited amount of oxidation of the surface of the chromium particles to improve bonding. Various other combinations of metals and oxides with alumina have been made, for example chromium-molybdenum-alumina-titania. The use of cermets based on silica, mullite or kyanite as high-temperature friction materials for such applications as the clutch and brake linings of aircraft have been reported. Thorium-oxide—tungsten cermets are extensively used as cathode cylinders in magnetron valves.

As regards (*ii*) the carbides of the fourth, fifth and sixth groups of the Periodic Table are wetted by iron, nickel and cobalt, forming strong bonds, and cermets of these are thus easier to produce. Their high-temperature load-bearing strength is not so good however. Both titanium carbide and tungsten carbide-based cermets are widely used. Tungsten carbide-metal infiltrated cermets have been investigated for use in turbine buckets and blades, while titanium carbide-steel cermets have been produced which are heat-treatable and machinable in the annealed condition. Titanium carbide cermets have particularly high impact strength and oxidation resistance ; in the United States intensive efforts have been made to improve their performance for use in jet engines.

(*iii*) There are a few commercial boride-based cermets, e.g. chromium boride with molybdenum or chromium-molybdenum alloys, which can be used up to 1450°C., and have extremely high strength at high temperatures. Other products include chromium boride with nickel, and titanium boride with iron, nickel or cobalt. Cermets based on silicides and nitrides are said to resemble those based on borides, but they are still in the experimental stage.

Cermets are used for numerous purposes in nuclear reactor technology, particularly for fuel elements, in the form of 'matrix' or 'dispersion' units (see Section 12.1). Other nuclear uses include control rods and container materials such as zirconium oxide-titanium.

Although cermets have proved useful in a number of fields, it must be said that progress so far has been rather disappointing on the whole.

12.2 Nuclear energy[2]

12.2.1 Types of nuclear reactor

Natural uranium contains 0.7% of the fissile isotope U_{235} and 99.3% of U_{238}, which is non-fissile but fertile, i.e. it can be made use of by converting it into plutonium, which is fissile. There are two main categories of reactors : 'thermal' and 'fast' reactors. The former comprises most of those built so far, and makes use of neutrons that have been slowed down to thermal energies by passing them through moderators. These 'thermal' neutrons produce the further fission of U_{235} necessary to produce the chain reaction, and also convert some of the U_{238} to plutonium. In the other type of reactor the neutrons are used without a moderator, to 'breed' plutonium, the fuel being enriched with U_{235} or Pu. Most nuclear power stations employ thermal reactors, e.g. Calder Hall, Berkeley-on-Severn, and the Advanced Gas Reactor (AGR) now being built at Dungeness. The Dounreay reactor is of the breeder type.

The heat produced by the nuclear fission is transferred, via a heat exchanger, to high pressure steam, which is used for driving a turbogenerator. Heat exchanger materials include water (Hanford, U.S.A., and some Soviet reactors), air (Windscale), carbon dioxide (a series of reactors in line of succession from Calder Hall to Dungeness), and the liquid sodium-potassium eutectic which is liquid at room temperature (Dounreay). The efficiency of conversion of steam to electrical power of the Calder Hall reactor is about 25%, but by increasing the maximum steam temperature through successive stages in the later reactors, from 315°C. up to 650°C., it has been possible to increase the thermodynamic efficiency up to 41%, which is a 1% improvement on the best fossil-fuel station so far designed, and if still higher temperatures can be used even higher efficiencies should be obtainable. This trend towards higher temperatures has been the main stimulus to the use of ceramics in this field because of the higher operating temperatures possible compared with metals. Ceramics also form important components in other nuclear power systems such as those for propelling ships, submarines and rockets, and for providing power in remote locations and for space craft.

The principal parts of a reactor where ceramics are used are : (*i*) the fuel element ; (*ii*) the fuel container or 'can' ; (*iii*) the moderator ; (*iv*) control and safety rods ; (*v*) structural parts and ancillary equipment.

12.2.2 Fuel elements

These may be in the form of rods, pellets or other shapes, and the material may be (*a*) homogenous, i.e. containing pure fissile material or an alloy or mixture with some diluting material. (In the Calder Hall reactor there are 10,000 uranium rods encased in 'Magnox', an alloy of aluminium and magnesium, and inserted at 8 in. intervals in the graphite moderator) ; and (*b*) hetergeneous, in 'matrix' or 'dispersion' form, in which the fissile material is dispersed in the moderator material. This arrangement has the advantages of less susceptibility to damage by neutron irradiation and of high thermal conductivity.

Ceramics have the following advantages over metallic fuels :— (*a*) higher melting points ; (*b*) absence of phase changes (uranium metal has two such changes at 668 and 774°C., accompanied by large volume changes) ; (*c*) better resistance to coolants, particularly to liquid metals ; (*d*) better resistance to neutron irradiation. Disadvantages of ceramics lie mainly in their lower thermal conductivity, which gives high internal temperatures, and the lower density of fissile atoms. The comparatively low thermal stress resistance of ceramics, for example UO_2, may also become serious under more severe conditions.

The ceramics of most interest as fuel elements are the dioxide and monocarbide of uranium, the latter having the advantage over the former of higher thermal conductivity. Other possible compounds include the nitride and silicide of uranium, and the oxides and carbides of thorium and plutonium. One method of making UO_2 fuel elements is by fabricating into rods, inside the metal containers, as already described (10.8), using vibratory compaction followed by swaging. An alternative shape is small spheres or pellets. Ceramic dispersion type fuels include UO_2 dispersed in BeO, Al_2O_3,

MgO, and also in stainless steel as a cermet; uranium and thorium carbides dispersed in graphite (Winfrith 'Dragon' experimental reactor) or in SiC.

12.2.3 Fuel containers

Canning materials must interfere as little as possible with the passage of neutrons emitted from the fuel; comparatively light elements are most suitable. They must also be unreactive with the fuel or the coolant. The containers must be capable of being completely sealed to prevent the escape of radiocative gaseous fission products. Thin tubes of aluminium were used for the early reactors, but were superseded by Magnox which is stronger and can more easily be provided with deep fins for cooling. At the higher operating temperatures made possible by the use of uranium oxide, a metal of higher melting point became necessary, and beryllium and zirconium alloys and stainless steel are used. These are now being followed by ceramics in some cases; for example, in one form of dispersion element silicon carbide has been pyrolytically deposited around uranium carbide spherules. In fast (breeder) reactors, where liquid sodium-potassium is used as coolant, aluminium cannot be used as it would react violently, and therefore stainless steel or other non-reactive metals have to be used.

12.2.4 Moderators

The requirements as regards moderators are : (a) that the material shall have a low neutron capture cross section, i.e. that when neutrons interact with the atoms of the moderator there is only a small probability of their being captured, and thus lost as far as the chain reaction is concerned; and (b) that there shall be a comparatively large decrease in energy of the neutrons, e.g. from about 1MeV down to about 0.025eV, per collision with the moderator atoms, this being a measure of the efficiency of the material. Light elements are best, particularly beryllium, carbon, oxygen, hydrogen and deuterium. Graphite is probably the most widely used material; in the Calder Hall reactor the moderator core is 27 ft. high by 35 ft. in diameter and consists of 1000 tons of the purest graphite that can be made, in the form of an assembly of 58,000 separate pieces, each accurately machined. Water, heavy water, and a paraffin type of wax are also used at moderate temperatures, but for high operating temperatures beryllium oxide is of the most interest because of its favourable thermal, chemical and mechanical properties ; beryllium carbide is another possibility. These materials are also suitable for making dispersion type fuels, in which they form the matrices.

12.2.5 Control and safety rods

Since the function of these is to limit the availability of neutrons, a high neutron capture cross section is required. Metallic cadmium is used at present, but there are a number of ceramics of interest for this purpose, such as the refractory borides, hafnium oxide, some rare earth oxides, and the carbides and nitrides of boron and hafnium.

12.2.6 Structural parts and other uses

Various ceramics, particularly alumina, are used for structural parts. Other uses are : refractory insulating materials such as bubble alumina ; special glasses and ceramics into which waste products can be fused for disposal ; and crucibles in uranium oxide and in calcium fluoride, which are slip cast and used for the melting of metallic uranium.

12.2.7 Irradiation effects[3]

Neutrons, being small and electrically neutral, can penetrate a crystalline lattice easily, and as many as 10^8 atoms may typically be passed before a collision occurs. When this happens three effects are possible : namely,

(*i*) Ionisation, which merely changes the electron distribution temporarily.

(*ii*) Atomic displacement, which if the initial energy of collision is high enough, may cause the displaced atoms to displace others, until the energy is spent. The lattice defects so produced are the usual form of irradiation damage. Ionic crystals with simple structures show least damage ; anistropic structures and highly covalent crystals are more easily damaged. In some cases, for example alumina, there is little structural change, but the thermal conductivity is usually decreased. In some materials, including alumina and beryllia, there is a decrease in electrical resistivity. However, in most cases irradiation damage of this type is reversible by high temperature annealing.

(*iii*) Transmutation, which is the most extreme form of damage, resulting eventually in the disintergration of the material. In the case of beryllium for instance, part of the nucleus is removed, the end product being a gas, tritium, ^3_1H. Fortunately energies much higher than those normally used would be necessary to produce this form of damage, and under the conditions usual in reactors about a year's irradiation would cause only about 1 in 10^5 of the Be atoms to be transmuted. The main effect of irradiation on uranium oxide is the release of krypton and xenon.

12.3 Magnetohydrodynamic generation (MHD)[4]

In recent years attempts have been made, by various means, to increase the efficiency of conversion of heat into electrical energy by eliminating the intermediate step of steam-raising in order to drive turbogenerators. MHD is one of the more promising processes and is intended for use in conjunction with nuclear energy and also for 'topping up' supplies of electricity to the grid system, using conventional fuels. The process may be of the closed or open circuit type ; the latter appears at the moment to be of more immediate commercial interest. In this system hot gases from the combustion of paraffin, for example, are seeded with potassium sulphate to assist ionisation, and flow at a temperature of at least about 2250°C. and at high velocity through a duct, across which is maintained a powerful magnetic field. The latter deflects the electric current formed by the ionised gases, and this is collected by electrodes mounted inside the duct walls. In order to produce the high temperatures necessary the gases are exhausted through a brickwork regenerator which is later used to preheat the incoming combustion air.

The materials requirements for duct walls, electrodes and regenerator are very severe indeed, and represent a challenge to ceramists which has not yet been met. Duct walls must withstand erosion by the gases at high temperatures, as well as slag attack by the seed material, must be electrically insulating and mechanically stable. The electrodes must be refractory, and thermionic emission is required of the materials used in order to neutralise the space charge which is set up around them ; zirconium boride has been considered for this. Probably the least difficult problem is in finding refractories for the regenerator, but even here temperatures above 1200°C. are involved, and there is also the question of slag attack.

12.4 Gas turbine blades[5]

The temperatures up to which metals can be used are limited not only by their melting points but also by their tendency to creep, abrasion and oxidation. Much effort has been put into producing ceramic turbine blades, so far without much success. Silicon nitride and alumina have been used experimentally in a few instances where conditions were not too severe, but it appears that improvements in the refractoriness of nickel-based alloys still give them an advantage over ceramics in more severe conditions, such as those associated with rotor blades. These involve large centrifugal forces in addition to thermal shock and abrasion, and highlight the shortcomings of ceramics in general as regards their brittleness and relatively poor thermal shock and impact resistance. A small stone or other hard object drawn into the air stream might make a dent in a metal blade, but could easily break a ceramic one ; the effect would be cumulative, and the end product has been described as a 'heap of broken crockery' ! Another point is that turbine efficiency requires sharp trailing edges—very difficult to obtain with brittle materials. Cermets have been tried, but do not appear to have been successful so far. Ceramic fibres coated with metals may become a possibility.

12.5 Abrasives[6]

Something has already been said regarding the application of abrasives to the machining of ceramics (5.5) ; the manufacture of abrasive wheels, etc., is of course, an important section of the ceramic industry. The common abrasives are : diamond, boron carbide, emery (natural corundum), fused alumina, artificial corundum, sand, silicon carbide. Toughness, i.e. the ability to withstand high rates of impact, is as important as hardness. For grinding hard materials, a friable grain is best, since it maintains its angular cutting edges as fragments break away. Relative toughness and friability depend on various factors. For example, pure alumina grains tend to be very friable, but if they contain small additions of iron oxide or titanium oxide they become much more resistant to wear or fracture. Abrasive wheels may be either ceramic—or resin-bonded. The ceramic type contains clay and felspar, or other materials such as quartz, sodium silicate, frits, or phosphates. They are made by hydraulic dry pressing, vibration compaction, casting, etc., followed by firing. The friability of the product is specified as the 'grade', which can be controlled by varying the nature of the grain and bond, and by the relative amounts of the two. Porous wheels cut faster, run cooler, and give more space for chip clearance ; dense wheels are stronger and wear better. In general, ceramic-bonded wheels are used for heavy work, and the resin-bonded ones for lighter work where some flexibility is required.

12.6 Fibres[7]

Readers will be familiar with the naturally-occurring mineral fibres such as asbestos, which can be made into wool, yarn or cloth. Another common material is glass in similar forms. To meet modern high temperature demands a number of refractory ceramic fibres have been introduced, which can be used up to 1100°C. continuously, and up to 1600°C. or more for short periods. The first to be made, many years ago, were quartz fibres, now made by melting quartz rods in an oxy-hydrogen jet and blowing the molten silica into the form of wool. Apart from their high melting point, quartz fibres have greatly superior weathering and chemical resistance compared with glass fibres, and they show good thermal shock resistance and high electrical resistivity. (It should be noted that although the term quartz is used, the product is really vitreous silica). Another method of making vitreous silica fibres for insulating purposes in jet engines consists of leaching the other constituents out of glass fibres with acids. A commercial product is known as 'Refrasil', and is widely used both for thermal and electrical insulation, e.g. in muffle furnaces, soldering iron elements, and in the form of yarn in gas turbines, rockets, etc. Ceramic fibres are also made from fused alumina-silica materials such as kaolin, bauxite, kyanite and fireclays, e.g. 'Fibrefrax', obtained by fiberising mixtures of alumina and silica containing a small amount of modifying agent such as borax glass. The molten mix is poured in a slow stream which is struck at right angles by a jet of compressed air, forming a fine fibrous glass. Synthetic inorganic fibres based on other types of compounds, e.g. alkali metal titanates, are now available. Many products are composites with plastics or other materials.

12.7 Whiskers[8]

Thin hair-like crystals of metals have been known for some time to be the cause of failure of electrical condensers when they penetrate the insulant and produce a short-circuit. However, they are very interesting because they have quite exceptional strength, and moreover they are not confined to metals ; in fact almost any crystallization process can be controlled so as to yield whiskers, and in recent years many ceramic materials have been made in this form. The growth of whiskers is believed to take place stepwise by a process of screw dislocations of the crystal lattice, with new growth spreading systematically as a layer over the old surfaces. They can be produced from solids by stressing, from solution, and from the vapour phase. In the form in which crystalline materials are normally obtained their mechanical strength is frequently of the order of only a thousandth of that predicted from their atomic structure ; this is because of defects of various kinds, particularly Griffith cracks, first recognised as the cause of low strength in glass. The strength of whiskers approaches the theoretical value due to the absence of such flaws. (Note that when a flaw-free surface can be prepared, for example by carefully dissolving away the surface layers of a glass rod, extremely high strengths are obtained). Silicon nitride, silicon carbide and aluminium nitride are some of the ceramic materials investigated. Typical sizes of whiskers are one to two microns thick by a centimetre or so long, but much smaller and much larger sizes are obtainable. There is at present much activity directed towards reinforcing metals with ceramic whiskers, e.g. Ni-Cr alloys with alumina whiskers.

12.8 Inorganic polymers [9]

The upper temperature of use of purely organic polymers is about 250°C., although this may be exceeded as a result of considerable efforts being made in this direction. The introduction of silicon into the carbon framework has given us the silicones, but the ultimate temperature at which polymers containing carbon can be expected to operate appears to be about 600°C.

The term inorganic polymer is capable of differing interpretations. Taking an extreme view it would embrace almost any non-amorphous inorganic solid and indeed many liquids. This does not seem to be particularly useful, and a more restricted definition, which appears fairly generally acceptable, would include only polymers that are mainly linear, as the distinction between polymers and other macromolecules lies in the extent of crosslinking, so that inorganic crystals and glasses would be excluded. Inorganic polymers would thus be analgous to organic 'plastics'.

The more stable inorganic polymers are based on alternating elements in the chain, most of which can be taken from the first two short periods of the Periodic Table, in particular B, Al, C, Si, N, P, O and S. One of the main difficulties is the tendency to form cyclic compounds instead of long chains. Another problem is the ease with which many inorganic polymers hydrolyse at high temperatures. Linear polymers also tend to soften on heating. Relatively few systems have been thoroughly investigated, apart from polymers containing Si-O, Si-N and P-N bonds. As well as being potential refractories, inorganic polymers are being considered as intermediates from which refractory products can be obtained by crosslinking or decomposition by heat or hydrolysis, etc.

12.9 Glass-ceramics (devitrified glasses)[10]

Attempts to obtain homogenity and uniformity in ceramics have led to the development, pioneered by the Corning Company in America, of various types of devitrified glasses known as 'Pyrocerams' The idea of making polycrystalline materials from glass goes back some 200 years, when Réaumur obtained rather poor quality opaque porcelain-like products by the prolonged heat treatment of glass bottles. The modern technique consists basically of melting a glass of selected composition, containing a catalyst or nucleating agent completely dispersed in it. The melt is then shaped and cooled down to about 100°C. above its annealing temperature, e.g. 800°C., where nucleation takes place and is complete in about an hour. The temperature is then raised slowly to, say, 1200°C., where the viscosity of the glass is low enough to allow crystal growth. The temperature is maintained until at least 80% crystallization has been attained, after which the product is cooled down to room temperature. Close temperature control during processing is essential ; different products are obtainable by varying the temperature cycle. The nucleating agents must be soluble in the glass and have a somewhat similar crystal structure to the phase to be nucleated ; various materials have been used, including sodium fluoride, phosphorus pentoxide and phosphates, titanium oxide (particularly useful because it will nucleate a wide range of glasses), vanadium oxide, and some colloidal metals. In principle the technique may be applied to any mixture that can be cooled to a glassy state.

Glass shaping methods can be used, and the change in dimension during subsequent processing is small enough to enable very close dimensional tolerances to be obtained. The strength of the parent glass facilitates the manufacture of thin-walled articles which, if made by ceramic methods, would be very fragile in the unfired state. Other advantages of glass-ceramics are greater reproducibility, controllable crystal sizes even below one micron, and the possibility of obtaining products containing new crystal structures and combinations of crystals, with combinations of properties hitherto unobtainable. The range of glass-ceramics made commercially includes the following :—a cordierite (Pyroceram 9606) having good dielectric properties ; and a zero thermal expansion lithium aluminium silicate (Pyroceram 9608) used for tableware. Another product, Pyroceram 9609, contains extremely fine crystals and is covered with another layer of glass having much lower thermal expansion ; the latter is thus in strong compression, and the product has extremely high mechanical strength. Glass-ceramics have bending strengths typically from 10,000 up to 50,000 lb./in.^{2}, the latter being comparable to high-alumina. Also they can be made more refractory than most common glasses ; for instance it has been found that products made from the system $MgO-SiO_2-Al_2O_3-TiO_2$ can have deformation temperatures up to 1370°C.

Domestic ovenware has so far been the main commercial outlet for glass-ceramics, but rapid advances in their technology are being made, and the number of possible applications is multiplying, including road surfacing and other structural uses employing products made from metallurgical slags ("slagcerams"). In the United States a large number of missile radomes have been produced using one of the low expansion Pyrocerams containing cordierite. Glass-to-metal seals can be made by first coating the metal with the parent glass, which readily wets it, and the crystallisation can then be carried out, giving excellent adhesion. Apart from high temperature applications, with which we are mainly concerned here, glass-ceramics seem likely to play an important part in the electronics field, including micro-miniaturisation.

REFERENCES

1. "Cermets". J. R. Tinklepaugh and W. B. Crandall (Eds.), Reinhold Publishing Corp., New York, 1960.
2. (*a*) D. T. Livey, *Trans. Brit. Ceram. Soc.*, **56**,(9), 482, 1957.
   (*b*) Symposium on Nuclear Ceramics, *Trans. Brit. Ceram. Soc.*, **62**, 71—304, 1963.
3. F. J. P. Clarke, "Special Ceramics". P. Popper (Ed.), Heywood and Co. Ltd., London, 1960, p. 82.
4. R. A. Coombe, *New Scientist*, **13**,(272), 254, 1962.
5. E. Glenny, *Engineering*, **194**, Dec., 28, 1962, p. 852.
6. Anon, *Grinding Finishing*, **9**,(4), 34—38, 1963.
7. C. Z. Carroll-Porczynski, *Eng. Materials and Design*, July, 418, 1961.
8. J. E. Gordon, *Endeavour*, **23**,(88), 8, 1964.
9. (*a*) D. N. Hunter, "Inorganic Polymers". Blackwell Scientific Publications, Oxford, 1963.
   (*b*) P. Chantrell and P. Popper. "Special Ceramics 1964". Academic Press, London/New York, 1965.
10. (*a*) D. Stookey, *Chem. and Eng. News*, **39**,(25), 116, 1961.
    (*b*) P. W. McMillan. "Glass-ceramics". Academic Press, London/New York, 1964.

FURTHER READING

J. E. Hove and W. C. Riley (editors), "Ceramics for Advanced Technologies". John Wiley & Sons, 1955.

G. C. E. Olds, "New Ceramics". *Science Journal*, **2**, (8), 58, 1966.

CHAPTER 13

HIGH FREQUENCY CERAMICS

I—STEATITE

13.1 Dielectric losses—general

The development of broadcasting in the early 1930's brought with it new requirements in insulators and dielectrics that could not be met by porcelain at the comparatively high frequencies then beginning to be used.   Large high-frequency, high-voltage insulators were needed at transmitter stations for insulating the masts ; and the connections between transmitters and aerial assemblies, as well as electric generators and associated switchgear also involved many types of high-frequency insulators.   In addition, both transmitters and receivers required a variety of small insulators, condensers and coil formers.   The reason why porcelain could not be used is that its power factor, although satisfactory at mains frequency, causes unacceptable power losses at radio frequencies.   A note here on the significance of *power factor* may help the reader who is unfamiliar with the concepts involved.

In an ideal dielectric no electrical energy would be lost in an alternating electric field, since any energy absorbed in moving the (bound) charges in the material during any part of the cycle would be recovered in the reverse part of the cycle ; there would be no current **in phase** with the voltage and therefore no ohmic losses.   If current and voltage were represented as vectors rotating counter-clockwise, the current would always be a quarter of a cycle, i.e. 90°, ahead of the voltage (Fig. 13.1a).

In actual dielectrics losses do occur.   They are of two kinds : (*i*) *resistive* or *ohmic losses*, due to the fact that the resistivity, although high, is finite, so that there is a small net current in phase with the voltage ; and (*ii*) *absorptive losses*, which are complex and are due to internal friction associated with the movement of the electric charges in the alternating field.   The final result of both processes is the same—the conversion of electrical energy into heat.

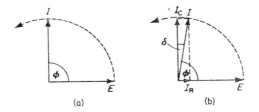

Fig. 13.1.—Power-factor. E—voltage ; I—total current ; I_c—capacitative current (90° ahead of voltage) ; I_R—resistive current (in phase with voltage) ; ø—phase angle ; δ—defect (or loss) angle.

An actual dielectric can therefore be represented as an ideal dielectric with a high resistance in series or in parallel.

The corresponding vector diagram is shown in Fig. 13.1b.

$$\text{Now } \textit{power factor} = \frac{\text{Power (dissipated as heat)}}{\text{Total volts x amps}}$$

$$= \frac{\text{Volts} \times \text{amps } \textbf{in phase}}{\text{Total volts} \times \text{amps}}$$

$$= \frac{EI_R}{EI}$$

$$= \frac{I_R}{I}$$

$$= \frac{I \cos ø}{I}$$

$$= \cos ø$$

$$= \sin δ$$

The *defect angle* δ should be very small, and in this case

$$\sin δ \ \simeq \ \tan δ.$$

Tan δ is normally quoted because it is obtained directly by the usual methods of measurement.

It can be shown that the actual *power lost, N,* in a dielectric is given by

$$N = 2\pi f E^2 C \tan δ$$

where f is the frequency and C the capacitance. For a capacitor of given dimensions, C is directly proportional to the dielectric constant K and the quantity $K\tan\delta$ is sometimes quoted as the *loss factor*. The fact that power loss is proportional to frequency accounts for the demand for very low power factors to compensate, at least partially, for the very great increase in working frequencies used in radio-communications. Actually, in most materials $\tan\delta$ itself falls off to some extent with increasing frequency, but this effect is of minor importance compared with the direct effect on power loss of increase of frequency. For example, porcelain with a power factor of, say, 200×10^{-4} (i.e. 2%) at 50 c/s and 80×10^{-4} at 1 Mc/s would give an increase of power loss at the higher frequency of

$$\frac{80 \times 10^{-4}}{200 \times 10^{-4}} \times \frac{10^6}{50}$$

i.e. an 8,000-fold increase.

The increased losses at the higher frequencies cannot be tolerated because : (*i*) at high voltages an excessive rise in temperature may occur ; and (*ii*) the resonance peaks of tuned circuits may become so flattened by the damping effect of the losses as to make sharp tuning impossible.

13.2 Steatite ceramics[1]

13.2.1 Talc as a dielectric

The very good insulating properties of fired block talc (steatite) had been utilised for some time before its application to radio ceramics, for a number of purposes, e.g. in the form of spacers and supports for electric lamp and valve electrodes. It is easily machined in the unfired state owing to its softness, and pieces retain their shape with little shrinkage when fired. These products are, however, porous and can only be used out of contact with air, but it was later found that non-porous ceramic products in which talc formed the major constituent could be made, which had only a fraction of the power factor of porcelain. The self-lubricating characteristics due to its platey structure made talc bodies particularly suitable for dry pressing, and thus for producing ceramic shapes to high precision. These considerations led to the introduction in the 1930's of a great variety of dry pressed steatite parts for use as insulators and capacitor dielectrics for the rapidly growing radio industry. In addition extruded and other plastically formed parts were produced, including high-frequency, high-tension insulators.

13.2.2 Ceramic compositions

The main characteristics of mineral talcs have already been noted (2.6). Talc on its own melts fairly sharply at about 1500°C., so that additions are necessary to enable ceramic articles to be fabricated. There are two types of steatite ceramics : *normal* and *low-loss* ; the former is fluxed with felspar and the latter with alkaline earths, which give higher T_e values (cf. non-felspathic porcelain) and, even more important, much lower power factors. Typical compositions are :—

Normal steatite		*Low-loss steatite*	
Talc	87%	Talc	75%
Ball clay	7%	Ball clay	15%
Felspar	6%	$BaCO_3$	8%
		$CaCO_3$	2%

Small amounts of other materials may be added, e.g. $MgCO_3$; also ZrO_2 and alkaline earth zirconium silicates, which are claimed to improve thermal shock resistance, although this is not often required. The clay assists in plastic shaping and also in fluxing. The content may be increased or decreased according to whether plastic shaping or dry pressing is to be used. However, increasing the clay/talc ratio narrows the firing range due to the formation of some cordierite, with its sharply melting eutectics. For this reason the clay content in normal steatites does not usually exceed about 10%, otherwise the firing range would become impracticably narrow. In low-loss steatites on the other hand this restriction does not apply, as the firing temperatures are much lower, due to the formation of various low melting-point eutectics between the alkaline earths, alumina and silica, e.g. BaO 28 : Al_2O_3 11 : SiO_2 61, which melts at 1175°C.

The fired body consists of crystals of magnesium metasilicate, $(MgSiO_3)$ and free silica, in a glassy matrix, the amount of the glass and its composition varying according to body formulation. It is important to know the analysis of the raw materials and to compound the body with care, particularly in the case of low-loss steatites, as the glassy phase has a great influence on firing and fired properties. When one of the more platey talcs is used the alignment of the platelets during extrusion[2], and to some extent in dry-pressing, can give rise to lamination, as well as differential shrinkage, and a substantial proportion of the raw talc is sometimes pre-calcined and milled. Variations in firing shrinkage may also be troublesome if close dimensional control is necessary, but it has been found that pre-pressing helps to randomise the platelet orientation in the final pressing[3]. (See also sections 4.2.3 and 5.2.6).

13.2.3 Manufacture

Most steatite ceramics made for low voltage applications are dry-mixed and dry pressed, using paraffin wax as the binder/lubricant, but in cases where parts are also made plastically the body may be wet mixed, unless a different composition is to be used for each method. Parts for high-tension insulators are made by extrusion followed by turning, as for porcelain. For low-tension insulators semi-wet pressing is used occasionally for complicated pieces. Steatite bodies can be slip-cast in an alkaline medium, but difficulties may be experienced owing to layering of the platelets in the cast.

For firing, white sand or soda-free alumina is satisfactory as a placing medium; another alternative is pure zirconia. The usual firing temperatures lie between 1250 and 1325°C. for low-loss steatites and between 1300 and 1375°C. for normal steatites, although sometimes temperatures up to 1400°C. are used, for example to fit in with the firing of Continental-type porcelain. Glazing is usually done after biscuit firing, using either lead or leadless glazes; occasionally the once-fired method is used with a leadless glaze, as for porcelain.

Difficulties were at one time experienced with low-loss steatites due to the fact that some articles which appeared perfectly satisfactory immediately after firing developed porosity, crazing of the glaze, and a tendency to disintegate, after storage. X-ray diffraction investigation showed that a slow crystalline change occurred after firing, and continued for a long time afterwards. When talc is heated it loses its combined water over a range of temperature from about 800 to 950°C., and its structure changes to a crystalline modification of magnesium metasilicate known as *enstatite*, plus free silica. Above 1000°C. enstatite changes to another form known variously as *protoenstatite, mesoenstatite* or *metatalc*. This is the high-temperature form, and on cooling it tends to change to a third modification, *clinoenstatite*; this change is very sluggish and unless suppressed completely is likely to continue over a long period and cause deterioration of the product[4]. It was found that the larger the protoenstatite crystals grew on firing the more rapidly the conversion occurred. Conversely, by keeping them very small, e.g. well below 7 microns, the conversion could be entirely suppressed for all practical purposes. The formation of too much liquid phase at the firing temperature, or prolonged or repeated firing, favours the formation of large crystals, with consequent instability. Talcs that are comparatively high in CaO will give more liquid phase, and in order to counteract this it may be necessary to reduce the amount of added $CaCO_3$ and of $BaCO_3$. Provided that the crystals remain small the glassy phase probably helps by mechanical stabilisation. It has been stated that small additions of $MnSO_4$ also stabilise protoenstatite[5].

13.2.4 Properties

Some of the more important properties of steatite ceramics are listed below.

Property	Unit	Normal steatite	Low-loss steatite
Tan δ (at 1 Mc/s)	$(\times 10^{-4})$	20—25	3—12
T_e	°C.	400—500	at least 800
Bending strength (plastically shaped)	lb./in.^{2} $(\times 10^3)$	14—22	10—18
Coefficient of linear expansion (20—600°C.)	°C.$^{-1}$ $(\times 10^{-6})$	7—8	8—10

Comparing these figures with those for porcelain (Table 7.3), it will be seen that steatite is superior in power factor and resistivity (at 300°C., for example, it is about two orders of magnitude higher), but although its mechanical strength is somewhat better, its higher coefficient of thermal expansion gives it rather poorer thermal shock resistance.

13.2.5 Products (See Plate III, facing page 116).

Steatite products include the following :—

A great variety of small insulators such as rods and tubes for use as stand-off and lead-through (bushing) insulators ; and plates, e.g. printed circuit bases. Many such parts are metallised : for example, bushings designed to have wires soldered into them, and to be soldered into a transformer tank, forming hermetic seals. Some larger insulators are made for high-tension work.

Coil formers, e.g. for radio-frequency tuning coils. Capacitors, e.g. small trimmer capacitors consisting of a rotor and a stator disc, each metallised in such a way that the capacitance can be varied by rotating the rotor.

13.3 Other low-loss ceramics

Several other ceramics having low power factors have been produced, mainly for special purposes requiring a combination of low loss and other properties such as thermal shock resistance. Some, like cordierite, zircon porcelain and alumina, have already been discussed. The remainder include the following :—

Forsterite, Mg_2SiO_4, which has found a limited application owing to its high coefficient of thermal expansion ($9 \times 10^{-6}/°C.$) ; this happens to be a good match for titanium metal and enables these two materials to be joined together to form satisfactory seals for certain special valves. Forsterite has a melting point of 1910°C. and good mechanical strength.

Wollastonite, $CaSiO_3$, which has a very low power factor and has been made into a dielectric with a power factor down to 1×10^{-4} by compounding it with carefully chosen lead frits.[6]

Another group of ceramics based on titanium oxide will be dealt with in the next Chapter.

REFERENCES

1. R. W. Batchelor, *Ceramics*, **9**, (115), 14, 1958.
2. T. F. Berry, W. C. Allen and W. A. Hassett, *Bull. Amer. Ceram· Soc.*, **36**, (8), 393, 1959.
3. R. S. Lamar, *J. Amer. Ceram. Soc.*, **27**,(11), 317, 1945.

4. E. C. Bloor, *J., Brit. Ceram. Soc.*, **1**,(2), 309, 1964.

5. J. F. Sarver and F. A. Hummel, *J. Amer. Ceram. Soc.*, **45**, (4), 152, 1962.

6. M. M. Bunag and J. H. Koenig, *ibid*, **42**,(9), 442, 1959.

CHAPTER 14

HIGH FREQUENCY CERAMICS

II—HIGH PERMITTIVITY CERAMICS

14.1 Miniaturization

The approach of the second world war saw the beginning of a rapid growth in the complexity of radiocommunications equipment, particularly for radar and other military purposes, which necessitated the accommodation of an increasingly large number of electronic components in very restricted spaces, in aircraft, tanks, etc. In more recent times the problem has become even more pressing with the advent of computers and space flight, so that we now speak not only of miniaturization but of microminiaturiaztion. Wire connections have been eliminated by the introduction of printed circuits on glass, ceramic or plastic bases, and even components themselves are now produced by vacuum evaporation on to glass or other substrates. Where capacitors, transformers and other components are made by more conventional methods their size has been drastically reduced, and of course many types of valves have been largely replaced by transistors.

Our main concern in this section is with *capacitors*. These have been reduced in size by the use of rolled paper and plastic film dielectrics, but *high permittivity* ('high-K') *ceramics* have also played an important part. Most insulating materials have permittivities not higher than about 10, for example those of porcelain, steatite, glass, mica and alumina lie in the range 4 to 9, but a few substances have long been known to have abnormally high permittivities. One of these, *rutile*, is sufficiently refractory and chemically stable to be capable of being fabricated into a ceramic product, and the obvious step was to try to make use of it for much smaller capacitors, since for a constant thickness of dielectric the area of the plates necessary for a given capacitance is inversely proportional to the permittivity of the dielectric. This was the starting point for the development of a whole range of high-K ceramics, culminating in some having permittivities running into tens of thousands, and the discovery of a number of other unusual and technically important properties. High permittivity results from a critical structural configuration, whereby electrical charges are very easily displaced by small potential differences, and sometimes even spontaneously ; both electronic and atomic displacements are involved.

14.2 Rutile, titanium oxide, TiO$_2$[1]

14.2.1 Properties

Rutile has a tetragonal structure and is therefore anisotropic. The permittivity parallel and at right angles to the long (c) axis is 170 and 90 respectively; in the polycrystalline form it averages out at 100 to 110. Other properties that make rutile interesting as a dielectric are : (*a*) its low power factor, which can be as low as 1—2 $\times$ 10^{-4}, and (*b*) its large *negative temperature coefficient of permittivity* (approximately −750 $\times$ 10^{-6}/°C.).

The significance of (*a*) is that its use as a dielectric at radio frequencies can be extended to tuned circuits handling quite high power, such as radio frequency oscillators for induction heating and for radio transmitters, the dielectric losses being low enough to avoid undue heating up or damping of tuned circuits. As regards (*b*), since most circuit components have a slight positive temperature coefficient of permittivity, a negative coefficient is useful in compensating for variations in the ambient temperature and thus avoiding frequency drift in tuned circuits. Moreover the temperature coefficient of rutile can be modified by suitable additions to give a whole range of values, from strongly negative to slightly positive.

14.2.2 Ceramic compositions

Either anatase or rutile may be used as starting materials (see 2.9). The patent literature abounds with recipes for titania bodies, and it would appear that the Periodic Table has been fairly thoroughly combed for additions for one purpose or another (one patent in fact covers the addition of elements ranging from nos. 59 to 72, i.e. nearly all the rare earths !).

The objectives in compounding rutile ceramics are :—
(*a*) high effective permittivity ;
(*b*) low power factor ;

(*c*)   a moderate firing temperature ;
(*d*)   adequate plasticity ;
(*e*)   modified temperature coefficients of *K*.

(*a*) When a material of higher permittivity is diluted with one of lower permittivity, the effective permittivity is lowered more rapidly than in proportion to the amount of diluent present. With some reservations the relation

$$\log K = n \log K_1 + (1 - n) \log K_2$$

holds, *K* being the effective permittivity of the mixture, K_1 and K_2 those of the components, and *n* the volume fraction of material of permittivity K_1. To take an example, a composition of 90 % by weight of rutile of *K* 120, and 10 % of clay of *K* 6, would give an effective *K*, calculated on the above basis, of only 73.4. A ceramic with a volume porosity of 10 % would have a similar value of *K*. Therefore, in order to maintain *K* as high as possible, the amount of clay or other normal inorganic materials must be kept to within a few percent, and the (sealed) porosity must be low (no open porosity is permissible).

(*b*) Titanium oxide readily loses oxygen at temperatures approaching its sintering temperature (1400—1450°C.). This leaves some free electrons which are capable of taking part in conduction, and consequently the power factor rises. The addition of fluxes which lower the sintering temperature will tend to reduce the loss of oxygen ; alkaline earths and clays have been used for this purpose. If, however, some of the Ti^{4+} ions can be replaced by ions of suitable size and of lower valency, e.g. Al^{3+}, there is one less electron available and the freeing of electrons in the oxygen-deficient TiO_2 is counteracted. Added in the form of clay, aluminium ions are effective in this way, and very good ceramic dielectrics are made by adding up to 5 % or so of a plastic clay, which also assists shaping and vitrification. Other compounds used include zinc oxide, which gives the Zn^{2+} ion and also assists vitrification. If, on the other hand an ion of higher valency is introduced, e.g. Sb^{5+}, the effect of oxygen deficiency is accentuated, semi-conduction is 'built-in', and free electrons remain even when there is no oxygen deficiency. (This principle is in fact used for other materials, in making transistors, etc.).

Another addition which has been made with the object of reducing power factor is zirconium oxide ; being a refractory oxide, the effect is probably to hinder the passage of electrons across grain boundaries.   Incidentally, it is desirable to avoid the growth of large crystals in TiO_2 ceramics, and ZrO_2 also helps in this way. The dependence of power factor on frequency is affected by additions and by methods of manufacture.

(c) This objective is normally achieved by additions of ball clay or bentonite, occasionally with other fluxes.   A typical body containing 5 % of plastic clay would vitrify in the region of 1350°C.

(d) Apart from ball clay or bentonite, it is usually necessary to use an organic plasticiser, particularly for extrusion.

(e) A large number of substances have been added to TiO_2 in order to give controlled temperature coefficients of K. Some merely act as diluents, e.g. ZrO_2, while others form compounds having different characteristics, e.g. MgO and BaO, which form titanates.   The TiO_2—BaO system has been used to a considerable extent to obtain a wider range of coefficients.

14.2.3 Manufacture

As indicated above, organic shaping aids are usually required, depending on the particular process used.   Many parts are made by extrusion and by dry pressing, while a few, including some quite large pieces, are made by isostatic pressing and turning.   Injection moulding is also used for complicated shapes.

Particular care is necessary in firing, in order to avoid reduction. Either white sand or alumina can be used for placing.

In making capacitors, the electrodes are formed by painting on silvering compositions, followed by firing at 600—800°C.   Disc capacitors are silvered on opposite faces, and tubular ones are silvered inside and out.   Contacts (tags) are soldered on, and in some cases a protective coat of paint is given.

14.2.4 Products

Capacitors fall into two types : *receiver* and *transmitter* types. In the latter type (known as 'Hi-loads') the power factor requirements are more stringent, since considerable radio frequency power has to be handled without undue heating up.   It may happen that the power factor appears satisfactory when no load is applied, but rises when a load is applied.   In extreme cases it has been known for the heat generated to be sufficient to melt the solder by which the tags were attached.   Transmitter capacitors are made in a number of shapes, the commonest being tubular, with one or both ends open, and with glazed flanges to increase the leakage path, at the open end(s).   In some cases metal cooling fins are attached.   Capacitances range up to 4,000 pF, and sizes up to 4 in. o.d. by $8\frac{1}{2}$ in. long, open at both ends, handling up to 150 kVA at 10 kV.

Receiver type are much smaller, and are usually in the form of tubes or discs.

14.3 Magnesium titanate, 2MgO. TiO$_2$—MgO.TiO$_2$

This is included, in spite of its having a K of only about 14, because of its use in modifying the temperature coefficient of rutile (magnesium titanate has a slightly positive coefficient), and because it can be used instead of rutile for transmitter capacitors, as its power factor is even better.

Magnesium titanate is made by calcining together titanium oxide and magnesium oxide. followed by milling.   It is compounded and fabricated in a similar way to rutile.

14.4 Calcium titanate, CaTiO$_3$

Although this compound has a K of about 150 and a low power factor, it has not found any important application by itself, but is sometimes used to modify the properties of other titanates.   Its temperature coefficient of K is $-1500 \times 10^{-6}/°C$.   It is prepared by calcining together calcium carbonate and titanium oxide, followed by milling, etc.

14.5 Strontium titanate, SrTiO$_3$

This is of greater interest than calcium titanate, having a permittivity of 240, and a very high temperature coefficient of K— about $-3000 \times 10^{-6}/°C$.   It also has a low power factor, is prepared in a similar manner to the other titanates, and is made into a ceramic composition by the addition of 1—3% of ball clay or bentonite.

It is used to a limited extent for radio receiver capacitors, but its high temperature coefficient of K means that it cannot be used where there is a wide variation in ambient temperature, although this property has been made use of for temperature measurement at very low temperatures. Its most important application is as an additive to other titanates.

14.6 Barium titanate[2], BaTiO$_3$
14.6.1 Properties

The systematic investigation of the additions of substances to titanium oxide with the aim of obtaining higher permittivities culminated in the discovery in 1944 of the remarkable properties of barium titanate—properties so remarkable in fact that since that time many hundreds of papers dealing with barium titanate and compositions containing it have appeared.

The permittivity is about 1400 at room temperature, falling slightly as the temperature rises, until about 70°C. when it begins to rise rapidly to a value of several thousands at 120°C. Above this temperature it falls off rapidly. This behaviour is intimately connected with its crystal structure, which is similar to that of the mineral *perovskite* (CaTiO$_3$), i.e. ideally a cube with the divalent cation at the body centre. The Ti ions are at each corner, with an octahedron formed by six oxygens surrounding each Ti ion. From geometrical considerations it can readily be shown that the radius of the divalent cation should ideally be about 1.40Å in order to fit perfectly within the Ti-O framework. The ionic radius of Ba is 1.52Å, i.e. it is too large to be a perfect fit, and careful X-ray studies showed that at room temperature the structure is not truly cubic but tetragonal ; as the temperature rises the shorter (a) axis expands while the longer one (c) contracts, until at about 120°C. they become equal, so that the structure above this transition temperature is truly cubic. The process is readily reversible on cooling, although there is actually a small range of temperature around 120°C. where the two crystal forms coexist. Other crystal inversions take place on cooling below room temperature—tetragonal-orthorhombic at 5°C., and orthorhombic-rhombohedral at −90°C.—each accompanied by an anomaly in the permittivity.

Other unusual properties of barium titanate are :—

(a) Strong applied electric fields decrease the permittivity, which falls to about half its initial value when the field strength reaches 4kV/mm. At the same time the transition temperature is slightly raised. With ordinary dielectrics the charge (or polarisation) induced varies linearly with applied voltage, e.g. doubling the voltage doubles the charge on the plates of a capacitor, because the permittivity is constant ; but in the case of barium titanate the relationship is *non-linear* up to 120°C., and shows *hysteresis* and *saturation* effects reminiscent of magnetisation curves. Further, even when the voltage is reduced to zero, there is still some *remanent polarisation*, which means that under suitable conditions barium titanate can be permanently polarised. Above 120°C. all these effects disappear.

(*b*) Barium titanate, when polarised, is *piezoelectric*, i.e. a mechanical strain causes a change in polarisation, and electric charges appear on opposite faces of the piece, the polarity depending on the direction of the mechanical deformation. The *inverse piezoelectric effect* also occurs, mechanical strain being produced by an applied electric field. Other substances like quartz and Rochelle salt were already well known as piezoelectrics, but barium titanate was the first ceramic material of this type to be produced.

Because it behaves in a somewhat analagous way to ferro-magnetic materials, the term "ferroelectric" has been applied to barium titanate and other similar substances discovered since. However, it must be borne in mind that there are fundamental differences, since magnetic polarisation is due to the alignment of unbalanced electron spins, whereas electric polarisation is due to the alignment of electric dipoles. As in the magnetic case barium titanate consists of small *domains* which are *spontaneously polarised*, i.e. within each domain the dipoles are aligned parallel to one another and all in the same direction up to the transition ('Curie') temperature It should be noted that in a ceramic piece there is no net polarisation unless it is artificially polarised by an electric field, because the domains are orientated at random, so that their individual polari-sations cancel out. It is interesting that these domains, which may be of the order of a mm., can be observed when thin crystals of barium titanate are viewed through a polarising microscope, and the boundaries seen to move when pressure is applied. The origin of the dipoles is a very small displacement from symmetry of the Ti and O ions in the crystal.

Some of the hopes that were entertained when barium titanate was discovered have not been fulfilled because of its rather high power factor, which is of the order of 2 % ; this means that it cannot be used in tuned circuits. Other difficulties are that its dielectric strength is low and not easily reproducible, and it suffers from a gradual decrease in permittivity over a long period of time after manufacture (ageing), due to a slow change in domain orientention.

14.6.2 Modified barium titanate

The sensitivity of barium titanate to the presence of other substances is not entirely a disadvantage, for many useful modifications of its properties can be made, and in fact barium titanate is seldom used alone except for single crystal work. Some of the modifications are as follows :—

(i) The addition of substances of a similar (perovskite) structure and which form solid solutions with barium titanate alters the transition temperature without affecting the height of the peak permittivity. For example, strontium titanate lowers the 120°C. transition temperature in proportion to the amount added, and at about 28 % addition the peak is shifted down to room temperature. Most of these additions lower the transition temperature, an exception being lead titanate, which raises it.

(ii) The maximum can be flattened by certain additions, so that one can ensure that the permittivity, although considerably lower at its maximum, will not fall below a stated value over a wide working range of temperature. A great many different additives have been used for this purpose, e.g. fluorides, zirconates, bismuth titanate.

(iii) At the same time as altering the K-temperature curve various additives will reduce the power factor, generally by forming a glassy phase yielding a ceramic with very small crystallites, e.g. cobalt oxide, or by altering the structure so that the domains become locked in position and cannot move so readily under an applied field, e.g. magnesium either as the oxide or the fluoride. Nickel and iron oxides have also been found useful in this way. However, a compromise has to be made between high permittivity and low power factor. (It is usually found that if one works above the transition temperature the power factor drops to quite a low value, but the temperature coefficient of K is apt to be strongly negative). One commercial composition used for capacitors contains sufficient strontium titanate to reduce the transition temperature below 0°C., and a little magnesium oxide ; the value of K varies from 5000 at 0°C. to 3000 at 100°C., and the power factor is about 0.2%.

14.6.3 Manufacture of barium titanate-based ceramics

The usual method of body preparation is to mill together commercially pure barium carbonate and anatase, together with the additives, then to calcine at around 1100°C. and remill in the normal way. An alternative procedure which has been used for preparing very pure material is by co-precipitation as barium titanyl oxalate, followed by calcining, etc.

Small clay additions are usual, in order to assist in shaping and to lower the vitrification temperature, as in the case of rutile, from over 1400°C. down to about 1350°C. or rather lower. The restriction on the amount of such additions, because of the consequent decrease in the effective permittivity, applies here with even greater force than in rutile ceramics.

The system BaO-TiO$_2$ is quite complex and includes several compounds, crystalline modifications and eutectics ; this, as well as sensitivity to traces of other substances and to firing conditions, accounts for much of the difficulty which has been experienced in obtaining reproducible properties in barium titanate-based ceramics. The precise ratio of BaO to TiO$_2$ has considerable effect on the final properties, particularly on power factor. The calcination is also critical, and the presence of mineralisers, whether accidentally or intentionally present, influences the final crystalline size, which has an important bearing on remanent polarisation and power factor, etc. It is estimated that there are some 89 variables involved in the manufacture of barium titanate ceramics.

Extrusion and dry pressing are the main shaping techniques, but barium titanate ceramics are also made in the form of thin sheets (9.4.5).

Single crystals up to an inch or more in length have been grown from melts of barium titanate in barium fluoride or in potassium fluoride containing small amounts of iron oxide for example, by careful cooling and also by withdrawing a seed crystal at a very slow, controlled rate from the melt. Single crystals, although used mainly for research purposes, have also been used for some technical applications.

Barium titanate, like rutile, must be fired in an oxidising

atmosphere, in order to minimise the tendency to reduction of Ti^{4+}. The only satisfactory placing material appears to be zirconium oxide (see 10.6) due to the reactivity of barium titanate with silica, and to a less extent with alumina.

14.6.4 Products[3] (See Plate III, facing page 116)

High K capacitors are produced by the million in the form of tubes and discs, for applications where a rather poor power factor can be tolerated, mainly in decoupling and smoothing capacitors for the high tension supplies of radio and television sets and for suppressing radio interference from electrical appliances. Another form of capacitor is produced as a high capacitance unit by taking pieces of thin film, 0.007 in. thick, making capacitors by coating with metal, e.g. platinum, palladium or nickel, stacking these units on top of one another, pressing the stack together and then firing. By connecting the units in parallel, capacitances of the order of a microfarad can be obtained. Stacked film capacitors are expensive to produce but do have a limited application due to the virtual absence of stray inductance. Many capacitors having special characteristics such as flat K-temperature curves down to sub-zero temperatures, and others having special voltage—or temperature-dependent properties are produced.

Much higher capacitances can now be obtained, for certain limited fields of application, by the use of "barrier-layer" dielectrics. These are made, for example, from $Ba/SrTiO_3$ in the hexagonal crystal form, by a simple reduction-oxidation technique, whereby a surface layer of much higher resistivity than the bulk (reduced) material is formed, giving an extremely high effective K[4].

Piezoelectric devices. In order to make use of the piezoelectric properties of barium titanate it must first be polarised by raising the temperature above the transition point and applying a strong unidirectional electric field, then allowing the piece to cool down to room temperature still in the field. In this way it is possible to align about three-quarters of the domains and so obtain a net polarisation which is sufficiently permanent for practical use to be made of it. In order to minimise the tendency to depolarise, a few percent of lead titanate is added, which raises the transition temperature. An alternative type of piezoelectric ceramic which is now widely used is lead zirconate-titanate (14.7.2).

Piezoelectric devices fall into two groups : (a) those that convert mechanical energy into electrical energy and, (b) those that generate mechanical (ultrasonic) energy[5]. Both are known as *electromechanical transducers.*

(a) The most important application of this group is the well-known gramophone pick-up element. This is made in the form of a 'sandwich' or 'bimorph', and consists of two thin plates of ceramic, $\frac{1}{2}$ in. by $\frac{1}{16}$ in. by $\frac{1}{64}$ in., soldered on to opposite sides of a thin copper strip. The pieces are polarised transversely in opposite senses so that the movement of the stylus puts one piece in tension and the other in compression, about the neutral plane of the copper strip. The voltages generated in the two pieces are thus additive. An average output of about 1 volt can be obtained. Although this is not so good as with the older type of pick-up crystal, Rochelle salt, and necessitates an additional amplifying stage, ceramic elements have the advantage of being non-hygroscopic and thus of not requiring protection from contact with the atmosphere.

Other mechanical-to-electrical applications are hydrophone elements consisting of large blocks of ceramic silvered on opposite faces, employed in underwater detection ; and accelerometers, consisting of blocks or bars, also silvered on opposite faces, which when stressed by sudden acceleration develop a voltage proportional to the acceleration, and are used in the vibration and drop testing of metals and other materials.

(b) Ceramics used for generating mechanical energy must have a much lower power factor than those of the other group, otherwise the generator would heat up excessively during use. These devices are also made in block form and are widely used for generating ultrasonic power. They can be made to resonate at one of their natural frequencies in longitudinal, thickness or radial modes ; these frequencies usually lie between 20 and 1000 kc/s. When immersed in liquids violent agitation leading to cavitation, i.e. the formation of small evacuated cavities, can be produced ; the main use of this effect is in cleaning small articles such as watch parts, small ball races and sensitive valves. The cleaning is so efficient that it has been found necessary to apply a little stearic acid to the cleaned parts before they can be wetted with lubricating oil.

In conjunction with a detector unit, generators are used for underwater signalling and detection (e.g. ASDIC) ; they are also used in the fishing industry for detecting shoals of fish.

Other applications of interest, although of doubtful commercial success, include piezoelectric transformers which operate by converting electrical to mechanical oscillations, and then reconvert these to electrical oscillations. The impedances of the input and output are adjusted by choosing suitable electrode areas, and hence the piece can be used as an impedance matching device or transformer.

14.7 Other ferroelectrics

14.7.1 Lead titanate

Following the discovery of barium titanate, other compounds of similar structure were prepared and investigated to see whether they would also show ferroelectric behaviour. One of the more important is *lead titanate*, which has been mentioned as an additive to barium titanate. It has a permittivity of about 100 at room temperature, but there is not much practical interest in using it alone.

14.7.2 Lead zirconate

At room temperature and under low electric stress, although its K is about 100, this compound is actually *anti-ferroelectric*, its dipoles being aligned anti-parallel to one another ; however, under high electrical stress, or at temperatures near its transition temperature of 232—236°C., the dipoles become aligned parallel to one another forming spontaneously polarised domains, and the usual ferroelectric effects appear. There is only a small difference in free energy between the ferroelectric and anti-ferroelectric states, and the addition of as little as 3% of lead titanate makes it completely ferroelectric. This is the basis of the 'PZT' piezoelectric ceramics already mentioned. The permittivity is, however, much lower than that of barium titanate, being less than 800 at room temperature, but by replacing part of the ZrO_2 by SnO_2 permittivities of up to 1100 can be obtained, and by partial replacement of Pb by Ca or Sr, still higher permittivities can be obtained, e.g. a K of 1325 using the composition $Pb_{0.875}Sr_{0.125}$ $(Zr_{0.54}Ti_{0.46})O_3$.[6] Further improvements have been obtained by hot pressing, which avoids large grain growth and makes the maintenance of stoichiometry easy

—a point of practical importance since lead compounds tend to volatilise during calcining and final firing[7].

14.7.3 Niobates and tantalates

The Nb and Ta ions, although carrying a charge of $+5$, are of roughly the same size as the Ti^{4+} ion. If now the divalent cation, e.g. Pb^{2+} or Ba^{2+}, is replaced by a monovalent one of suitable size to fit into the cubic framework of Nb^{5+} or Ta^{5+} and O^{2-} ions, electrical neutrality will be maintained; i.e. instead of a compound $A^{2+}B^{4+}O_3^{2-}$ we shall have $A^{1+}B^{5+}O_2^{2-}$. It has been found that both *sodium* and *potassium niobates* show ferroelectricity (or anti-ferroelectricity in the case of the sodium compound), and some commercial use has been made of these.

14.7.4 Gallates

Similar considerations regarding structure apply here, but since the Ga ion carries a charge of $+3$, another trivalent ion is required; lanthanum is found to be suitable, and the compound $La^{3+}Ga^{3+}O_3^{2+}$ is ferroelectric.

14.7.5 Tungstic oxide, WO_3

This can be regarded as derived from $BaTiO_3$ by replacing the Ti^{4+} ions by W^{6+} ions and omitting the Ba^{2+} ion so that electrical neutrality is maintained. This compound is anti-ferroelectric and is not of much interest as a dielectric because of its rather high electrical conductivity.

14.7.6 Other structures

Although the perovskite structure favours the formation of ferroelectrics it is not essential, and a number of compounds not of that structure have been prepared which are ferroelectric; for example cadmium niobate, $Cd_2Nb_2O_7$, which has the ilmenite structure. It would appear that the essential structural condition for ferro-electricity is linked octahedra of oxygen ions, with a small cation in the centre (except in the case of WO_3). A slight degree of distortion from symmetry also seems necessary, with a very slight energy difference between two configurations.

REFERENCES

1. B. E. Waye, *Ceramics*, **10**, 12, 1958.
2. M. C. McQuarrie, *Bull. Amer. Ceram. Soc.*, **34**, 169, 225, 256, 295, 329, 1955.
3. D. S. Campbell, *ibid.*, **38**,(3), 16, 1959.
4. R. M. Glaister, *Proc. Inst. Electr. Engnrs.* (London), Pt. B, **109**,(22), 423—31, 1962. (Supplement).
5. K. Littlewood, *J. Roy. Inst. Chem.*, **86**, 78, 1962.
6. F. Kulcsar, *J. Amer. Ceram. Soc.*, **42**,(1), 49, 1959.
7. A. J. Mountvala, *Bull. Amer. Ceram. Soc.*, **42**,(3), 120, 1963.

FURTHER READING

International Conference on Components and Materials Used in Electronic Engineering, 1961. *Proceedings of the Institution of Electrical Engineers.*, **109**, Part B, Supplement No. 22, 1962.

"Ferroelectric Ceramics", Déri, Maclaren & Sons Ltd., London, 1966.

CHAPTER 15

HIGH FREQUENCY CERAMICS

III—MAGNETIC CERAMICS (FERRITES)

15.1 Development of ferrite ceramics

The use of high frequencies in radio communications led not only to a demand for special dielectrics but also for new types of magnetic materials to replace iron in transformer and inductor cores. As in the case of dielectrics the higher the working frequency the more serious do losses in the material become. Energy losses in a magnetic material in an alternating field cause the induced flux to be out of phase with the magnetising field and are a source of distortion. In order to reduce energy losses iron cores for use at mains frequency are laminated, and the laminae insulated to restrict the flow of eddy currents induced by the alternating field. When the operating frequencies were increased to over a kilocycle the subdivision of the core was taken a stage further by using iron powder, insulated and bonded with a thermosetting resin. Although iron dust cores have lower power losses the reduction has to be obtained at the expense of diluting the magnetic properties.

The ideal solution to the problem is a magnetic material which is itself an insulator. The earliest known magnetic material, *magnetite*, Fe_3O_4, has a much lower electrical conductivity than iron but not low enough to be useful. It has the *spinel* structure and can be regarded as *ferrous ferrite*, $FeO. Fe_2O_3$ (cf. $MgO. Al_2O_3$). The reason why it is not a good insulator is connected with an interchange between the two valencies of iron, giving rise to so-called 'hopping conductivity'. However, by replacing FeO by certain other oxides in which the metal ion is divalent and of about the same size as iron a series of highly insulating magnetic ceramics was developed in Holland towards the end of the last war, being first put on the market in 1947. Since that time the variety and applications of ferrites have been greatly extended, and today the frequencies at which they can be used range from zero (permanent magnets) up to the infra-red.

158

15.2 Properties

15.2.1 Magnetisation and permeability

The more important magnetic characteristics that determine the usefulness of magnetic materials are defined by the relationship between the *induced flux B* and the applied magnetising force *H*. Fig. 15.1 shows some *hysteresis loops* obtained as the magnetising force is varied. The *permeability* μ, i.e. the ratio of *B* to *H*, varies according to the position on the curve, and this must be specified in making comparisons between materials ; the *initial permeability* μ is commonly quoted. Naturally the higher the permeability the smaller the physical size of components such as radio transformers and inductors needs to be.

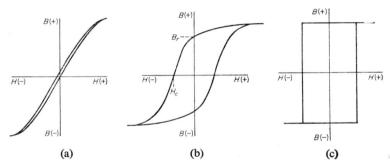

(a)   (b)   (c)

Fig. 15.1.—Hysteris loops. (*a*) Soft magnetic material ; (*b*) Hard magnetic material. Note large remanence and coercivity ; (*c*) Rectangular loop (ideal).

It will be seen from curve (b) that when *H* is reduced to zero some flux is retained (*remanent induction B_r*), and a negative magnetising force (*coercive force H_c*) is required to reduce the induction to zero. The hysteresis loop is dependent on the value of the maximum magnetising force used in the cycle, and a family of loops can be obtained by varying the value of H_{max}. A relatively wide loop would represent the behaviour of a *hard magnetic material* as used for permanent magnets, while a narrow loop would imply a *soft magnetic material*.

When the temperature of a ferromagnetic material is raised

the permeability increases up to a maximum at the *Curie temperature* and then falls off rapidly, the material ceasing to be ferromagnetic. On cooling below this temperature the material again becomes ferromagnetic, although any remanent magnetism will have been destroyed. In a non-ferromagnetic ferrite like zinc ferrite however, the permeability falls continuously with rise of temperature. By adding zinc ferrite to a ferromagnetic ferrite it is possible to shift the Curie temperature of the latter towards room temperature, thereby obtaining higher values of permeability. The *temperature coefficient* of permeability is of considerable practical importance and is usually specified.

For *permanent magnets* the material should possess :—

(*i*) High coercive force to prevent demagnetisation when used in motors, magnetic chucks and other situations involving strongly demagnetising conditions.

(*ii*) High resistivity to enable it to be used in high-frequency alternating fields without giving rise to eddy-current losses.

The *maximum value of $B \times H$, $(BH)_{max}$*, on the demagnetisation curve is used as a figure of merit. This is because the available magnetic energy in the air gap of the magnet is proportional to (volume of magnetic material) $\times$ (*BH* obtained at the working point on the demagnetisation curve), so that the material with the highest value of BH_{max} is likely to yield a smaller magnet for the same available energy.

15.2.2 Energy losses

For various reasons higher permeability is often accompanied by higher energy losses in the material. These comprise : (*i*) *hysteresis losses* (the area enclosed by the loop is a measure of these), which vanish at small amplitudes of the magnetising force ; (*ii*) *eddy-current losses*, which are usually small in highly insulating materials ; and (*iii*) *residual losses*, associated with the atomic and crystal structure. The last type is the predominant source of loss in ferrites. The *loss factor*, $\tan\delta.1/\mu$, or $1/\mu Q$ ($Q=1/\tan\delta$), is used to characterise the material with respect to magnetic losses, the lower this value the better the material is. The loss factor increases with frequency, so that a material may be satisfactory over one range of frequencies but unsatisfactory over others.

15.3 Types of ferrites
15.3.1 Spinel types

Like magnetite, most of the commercial ferrites have the spinel structure. This is cubic and contains metal ions both in four-fold coordination within O-*tetrahedra*, and in six-fold coordination within O-*octahedra*. There appear to be several possible distributions of the various metal ions in the crystal sites. In one case—'normal' spinels—the divalent and trivalent metal ions occupy the tetrahedral and octahedral respectively ; in another case— 'inverse' spinels—the tetrahedral sites are occupied by half the total trivalent metal ions, whilst the octahedral sites are occupied by the divalent ions and the remainder of the trivalent ones. All the simple ferrites of the spinel type are inverse and are ferromagnetic with very few exceptions, in particular those of zinc and cadmium, which are normal and non-ferromagnetic.

There are three main types of commercial composition : (*i*) *manganese-zinc ferrites*, (*ii*) *nickel-zinc ferrites*, and (*iii*) *magnesium-manganese ferrites* having a *rectangular hysteresis loop*.

(*i*) These have values of μ_i between 650 and 2,300, with low losses at frequencies up to about 1 Mc/s. A typical composition to give a permeability of about 2,000 is :—

MnO	27 mol %
ZnO	20 mol %
Fe_2O_3	53 mol %

By varying the proportions slightly, different characteristics within a certain range can be obtained. It will be noticed that there is a slight stoichiometric excess of Fe_2O_3 in the above composition. The reason for this is connected with the effect of *magnetostriction*, which may be either positive or negative, but which in either case tends to neutralise the magnetising field and so decrease the permeability. It was found that, with the exception of magnetite itself, which has a comparatively large positive magnetostriction, all the simple ferrites have a negative magnetostriction. By having a slight excess of Fe present the negative magnetostriction of Mn and Zn ferrites can be counteracted, and the resultant magnetostriction reduced to a very low value, giving a considerable increase in permeability, although at the expense of a lower resistivity.

(*ii*) *Nickel-zinc ferrites* usually contain just 50 mol % of Fe_2O_3, a typical composition being :—

NiO	32 mol %
ZnO	18 mol %
Fe_2O_3	50 mol %

They have a high resistivity but large values of magnetostriction, and consequently lower permeabilities than manganese-zinc ferrites. The above composition would give a permeability of the order of 100. At high frequencies very high permeability is not normally required, and the freedom from eddy-current loss makes these ferrites useful up to 20 Mc/s. By modifying the composition, e.g by increasing the proportion of Ni to Zn, the useful range of frequencies can be extended to the *microwave* region, i.e. over 1000 Mc/s, although the permeability may then be less than 20.

(*iii*) Both types (*i*) and (*ii*) are soft magnetic materials ; type (*iii*) is slightly hard. Commonly used compositions are manganese-magnesium, manganese-copper, and lithium-nickel ferrites ; one typical manganese-magnesium ferrite is basically :—

MnO	7 mol %
MgO	52 mol %
Fe_2O_3	41 mol %

The coercive force can be reduced if necessary by the addition of small amounts of zinc ferrite, but this reduces the switching time required to reverse the direction of magnetisation, which is an important consideration in the application for which this class of ferrites was developed—the storage of information in memory core units for high speed computers. (See section 15.5.3)

More recently a cobalt-ferrous ferrite has been introduced whose hysteresis curve is almost independent of the strength of the applied field, in contrast to the manganese-magnesuim-zinc ferrites which give minor loops at low fields.

Other ferrites include *nickel ferrite* alone, *manganese aluminium ferrite* and some containing Ni, Co, Mn and Al for certain microwave applications.

15.3.2 Hexagonal ferrites

When the divalent ferrous ion is replaced by one of larger size a modification of the spinel structure may occur, generally with the formation of a magnetoplumbite-type hexagonal lattice of complex structure. Barium behaves in this way, forming *barium hexaferrite*, $BaFe_{12}O_{19}$, an important permanent magnet material, because of its high coercive force (1700–2800 oersted), high resistivity (10^8 ohm-cm), light weight (density about 4.9 g/cc), and the cheapness and availability of the raw materials, since these do not include expensive ones like nickel and cobalt. Its magnetic properties depend on the way in which the individual crystals are aligned with respect to an applied magnetic field direction, the easiest direction of magnetisation being parallel to the hexagonal axis. A disc of polycrystalline barium ferrite will therefore be most easily magnetised in a direction perpendicular to its plane if it is made anisotropic by aligning the hexagonal axes of all the crystallites along this direction ; this is achieved by the application of a high static magnetic field during shaping (see 15.4.2). The addition of a third metal to barium ferrite, e.g. Zn or Mg, also enables the direction of easy magnetisation to be changed. Low losses can be obtained, with useful permeabilities up to much higher frequencies than in the case of the spinels.

15.3.3 Garnet type ferrites

The general formula of these is $3R_2O_3 . 5Fe_2O_3$, or $R_3Fe_5O_{12}$, where R is a rare earth metal, and useful materials have been developed on this basis, the most important being *yttrium-iron garnet*, $Y_3Fe_5O_{12}$. Garnets have a complex cubic structure, with 160 ions in the unit cell. They have the unusual property of being transparent to visible light, in addition to their magnetic properties. Their use is still in the early stages, but there are important potential applications in microwave techniques.

15.4 Manufacture
15.4.1 Preparation of materials

The raw materials used must be carefully selected and their chemical composition and physical characteristics closely controlled ; this is particularly true of iron oxide, on which a great deal of research has been carried out to relate its properties to those of the final product.

A very large proportion of commercially available ferrites are made by the conventional method involving the solid state reaction of oxides, carbonates, etc., by calcining the thoroughly mixed composition at temperatures ranging betweens 800° and 1300°C. Some alternative methods which have been ued on an experimental scale include chemical coprecipitation as the mixed oxalates or carbonates, and electrolytic coprecipitation, which allows the correct composition to be obtained by controlling the current.

The atmosphere during both calcining and final sintering influences the magnetic properties of the product. It is particularly important in the manufacture of manganese-zinc ferrites ; some reduction occurs during calcination followed by reoxidation on cooling. If the reoxidation is complete there will be competition with the binder for oxygen during the early stages of sintering, resulting in lower shrinkages and components with poor magnetic properties.

15.4.2 Shaping

The properties of the material at the shaping stage are particularly important and must be closely controlled ; the green density of the shaped piece is the main criterion of consistent material.

The most commonly used shaping method is dry pressing, the granulation of material for the dry pressing of tiny ferrite rings being one of the first applications to ceramics of the spray drying technique.

Extrusion is also extensively used, e.g. for manufacturing aerial rods. Various other shaping methods used include a form of wet pressing used for producing oriented barium ferrite components. This consists of pumping the material in slurry form into the die, and applying a magnetic field to align the particles, the compact being formed by a combination of pressing and vacuum filtration.

15.4.3 Sintering

Final temperatures range between 1200 and 1400°C. The sintering cycle for high quality manganese-zinc ferrite involves close control of the atmosphere as well as the temperature. A high oxygen content is required initially to burn out the binder, but at the cooling stage a low oxygen content is required to avoid reoxidation of the manganous and ferrous ions. There are many patents concerned with atmosphere control during sintering, and specially designed tunnel kilns are available for facilitating the introduction of nitrogen into the cooling zone.

15.4.4 Finishing

Some form of surface grinding is frequently necessary in order to achieve close mechanical tolerances for minimising the air gap between mating surfaces, e.g. sections of transformer cores, or to introduce a controlled air gap to give a specific magnetic permeability.

15.5 Products (See Plate IV, facing page 117)
15.5.1 Transformer and inductor cores

These constitute the largest use of ferrites, and are made from the magnetically soft ferrites (Mn-Zn and Ni-Zn ferrites). Shapes include :—

U-shaped cores for high-power transformers, mainly television line output transformers.

E-shaped cores for low-power transformers.

(Both U- and E-cores are used in pairs).

Deflection yokes for television tubes, in the form of large serrated rings, or split, specially shaped pieces of circular section. The material used is a grade of manganese-zinc ferrite.

Pot cores for wide-band communication transformers and for various types of inductors operating over the low, medium and high frequency ranges. These are cylindrical in shape and are made in sections to provide an annular space which accomodates the windings. The effective permeability controls the performance of inductors, e.g. the core loss and temperature coefficient of permeability are proportional to it, and it may be set to the required value by inserting during manufacture a small, precisely controlled air gap in the central part of the core.

15.5.2 Aerial rods

These are normally made from grades of nickel-zinc ferrite and are used in place of frame aerials in portable radio receivers, giving increased efficiency and a more compact unit. The aerial coil is slipped over the rod which acts as a core to intensify the magnetic field.

15.5.3 Magnetic memory cores

These are made in the form of small rings (toroids) down to $\frac{1}{8}$ in. or less in diameter, and possess nearly rectangular hysteresis loops—see 15.3.1 (c).   The principle underlying their use is briefly described as follows.   The system of numbers as used in computers is the binary system, in which zero and 1 are the only digits necessary to represent any given number.   For example, 13 (base of 10) would be represented as 1101, i.e. $2^3 + 2^2 + 0 + 1$, on the binary basis.   Now if magnetisation of the toroid in one direction is made to represent a 1, and in the other direction a 0, one can 'store' either digit by passing an electric pulse through a winding on the toroid, thus providing the appropriate magnetic pulse.   The direction of magnetisation can subsequently be determined, i.e. the stored 1 or 0 can be read back, by applying another magnetic pulse ; a pulse in the same direction would not change the state of magnetisation, but one in the opposite direction, if sufficiently strong, would reverse the direction of magnetisation of the toroid and give rise to an electrical impulse which could be detected.   This system will only work on condition that very little change in flux occurs until the coercive force is reached, at which point the direction of magnetisation suddenly reverses, giving saturation in the opposite direction ; hence the need for a rectangular hysteresis loop.

15.5.4 Permanent magnets

In applications where the shape is fairly simple and high performance is important, e.g. in loudspeaker magnets, anisotropic grades of barium ferrite are used, but there are many applications, such as multipolar magnets, where it is not practicable to orient the material, because of its shape, and isotropic (i.e. randomly oriented) grades are then used.   These are, of course, simpler to manufacture and therefore are more widely used than the anisotropic grades.   A recent application of barium ferrite on a large scale is for the pole pieces of motor car alternator generators.

15.5.5 Microwave applications

Many of these depend on the fact that an aligned spinning electron can be made to precess in resonance with an applied ultra-frequency field of the correct frequency.   The properties of the ferrite depend on the sense of the polarisation of the incoming electromagnetic vibrations relative to a steady applied field, and a variety of devices are based on this. Ferrites used include various spinel types and yttrium iron garnet, but for operation at millimetre wavelengths the steady field required is very high, and use has been made of the hexagonal ferrites so that only small additional external fields are required.

FURTHER READING

W. T. Dean, *Ceramics*, **10,** Oct., 8, 1958.

Proc. Brit. Ceram. Soc., (2), 1964.

CHAPTER 16

METALLISED CERAMICS

16.1 Reasons for metallising

The production of many electroceramic components involves the provision of metal coatings on the ceramic part. The object may be to provide (*a*) an electrically conducting coating, e.g. to form the 'plates' of a capacitor, the metallic 'winding' around a ceramic core to form an inductor, or the connections of a printed circuit on a ceramic base ; (*b*) a surface suitable for soldering or brazing, for attaching wires or sealing metal parts to ceramic parts ; or both.

16.2 Processes for parts used at normal temperature

For normal temperatures and clean atmospheres silver is the most commonly used metal owing to its good electrical conductivity and the ease of application and of soldering to it. Occasionly 'cold' silvering suspensions of flake silver, which merely require air-drying, are used for temporary coatings not to be soldered, e.g. test pieces for certain electrical measurements. Most silvering compositions, however, are fired on, usually at 700—800°C., and consist of flake silver or a silver compound such as the oxide, carbonate or resinate, incorporated with a flux such as lead borate, borosilicate or fluoride, together with a paint vehicle, etc., somewhat similar to the compositions used in pottery decoration. The paint may be applied by brush, wheel transfer silk screen, etc. In making capacitors a second and sometimes a third coat may be applied in which the ratio of silver to flux is increased in order to improve conductivity and so avoid increasing the power factor or decreasing the capacitance of the capacitor due to poor conductivity of the 'plates'. Drying and firing-on have to be done carefully to avoid blistering and carbonisation of organic compounds present.

Various soft solders may be used, a common one being the 63/37 tin/lead eutectic, to which a small addition of silver is made to minimise solution of the silver coating. Soldering is frequently done by dipping in a bath of molten solder ; this again must be done carefully to avoid damage due to thermal shock and stripping of the silver from the ceramic.

Platinum is also extensively used, particularly on steatite ceramics, for producing hermetic seals for connections into oil-filled transformers. In principle the method is similar to that used with silver. In soldering, great care is necessary in the choice of fluxes to obtain adequate wettability without damage to the platinum coating. A more recent alternative to platinum is nickel, applied as the oxide or other suitable compound, which is subsequently converted to the metal by firing in hydrogen or cracked ammonia.

16.3 Processes for parts used at elevated temperatures[1]

For higher temperatures such as are required in the operation of high-frequency power valves the usual method is the molybdenum-manganese process. A paint containing molybdenum powder with a small addition of manganese is applied to the ceramic (usually alumina). The coated piece is heated to a temperature approaching the softening temperature of the ceramic, e.g. 1700°C. for a high-alumina, in hydrogen, whereby the molybdenum becomes bonded to the surface. The manganese, which is known as an 'active metal', assists by improving the wetting of the surface, and there is also evidence that a chemical bond is formed, as manganese aluminate spinel has been detected and at temperatures as low as 800°C. some flux can be seen under the microscope.

The fired-on molybdenum is plated electrolytically with nickel or copper. The metallised ceramic is now ready to be brazed with a high-temperature solder such as the copper/silver eutectic, m.p. 780°C.; this again has to be done in a reducing atmosphere.

An alternative method sometimes used is known simply as the 'active metal process'. Like manganese, other 'active metals' such as titanium and zirconium, as well as their hydrides, readily wet ceramic surfaces and form strong bonds when fired in vacuo at about 900°C. Both high- and low-temperature solders can be used ; sometimes special solders with a titanium core are used for direct soldering on to ceramics.

Other methods of metallising employed in special cases include the vacuum evaporation and sputtering of gold and other metals. (These are becoming very important in relation to materials other than ceramics in the production of thin-film electronic circuits, as a result of the drive to greater and greater miniaturisation of components for computers, space craft and missiles. The size reduction achieved is spectacular, and densities of 2×10^6 components/ft.^{3} are readily obtainable).

16.4 High-temperature ceramic-metal seals[2]

There are three types of seal frequently used by vacuum engineers for valves and similar devices. These are :—

(*a*) The compression seal in which the ceramic part is sealed into a metal collar which contracts more on cooling than the ceramic, and forms a vacuum-tight seal, often without the necessity of metallising if a soft metal like copper is used ('crunch' seal).

(*b*) The butt seal in which the ceramic and metal are joined end to end. In this case it is necessary either to have accurate matching of the thermal expansions of the two materials, e.g. forsterite and titanium metal or, in line with more recent practice, to use metals that are rather higher in expansion, but sufficiently ductile to accommodate the mismatch, e.g. the Nilo type (Ni-Fe-Co or Ni-Fe alloys) or stainless steel, with alumina.

(*c*) The pin seal. Here a metal pin is brazed into a ceramic bush, etc. ; again the relative expansions are important. It is also important to ensure a very fine surface finish on the ceramic part. Seals are tested for vacuum-tightness, mechanical strength and ability to withstand high-temperature operation.

REFERENCES

1. C. A. Lindquist, "Electronic and Other Newer Ceramics". J. J. Svec, G. L. Vincent and K. A. Brent (Eds.), Industrial Publications Inc., Chicago, 1959, Chaps. 22—25.
2. W. H. Kohl, *Vacuum*, **14**,(9), 333—354, 1964.

APPENDIX 1

ELECTRICAL AND MAGNETIC DEFINITIONS

Capacitance (of a capacitor). The charge required to raise the potential difference between the plates by one unit. For a charge of 1 coulomb and a p.d. of 1 volt the capacitance would be 1 farad. As the capacitance range normally met with is many orders of magnitude less than a farad the microfarad ($\mu F = 10^{-6}F$) or the micro-micro- or pico- farad ($\mu\mu F = pF = 10^{-12}F$) is used. Capacitance is proportional to the area of the plates divided by the distance between them.

Coercive force, coercivity. The value of the reversed magnetic/ electric field required to reduce the intensity of magnetisation/ electric polarisation to zero.

Curie point. The temperature at which a transition occurs between ferromagnetic/ferroelectric states and paramagnetic/ paraelectric states. Above the Curie point spontaneously polarised magnetic/electric domains cease to exist.

Defect angle, δ. The complement of the phase angle, i.e. the angle by which the current vector fails to lead the potential vector by 90°C. $\delta = 90 - \phi$

Dielectric. An electrically insulating material, particularly the medium between the plates of a capacitor.

Dielectric strength, puncture strength, breakdown strength. The maximum electric stress, i.e. voltage gradient, that can be withstood without breakdown of a material by the passage of an electric discharge through it. Units : kV/mm, V/mil (0.001 in.), etc.

Electric polarisation, P. The electric moment per unit volume, i.e. the distance between the positive and negative charges multiplied by the value of the charges.

Electromechanical coupling coefficient (*or factor*), *k*, of a piezo-electric body.   The square root of the ratio of the electrical energy converted to mechanical energy over the applied electrical energy. A measure of efficiency of conversion.

Equivalent series resistance.   A capacitor may be represented as having a perfect capacitance in series with a resistance R $(= 1/\omega C \sin \delta$, where $\omega = 2\pi \times$ frequency, C is capacitance, and $\sin \delta$ the power factor).

Ferromagnetism/ferroelectricity.   The presence of spontaneously polarised magnetic/electric domains and the properties associated with these.

Inductance, L.   The e.m.f. produced in a conductor by unit rate of variation of current.   Unit : the henry (the e.m.f. in volts produced by a variation of current of 1 ampere per second).

Loss factor (*capacitance*).   The product permittivity $\times$ power factor, i.e. K tanδ

Loss factor (*inductive*).   The ratio power factor to permeability,

$$\text{i.e. } \frac{\tan\delta}{\mu} \text{ or } \frac{1}{\mu Q}$$

Magnetic flux, Φ.   The product of area by field strength. $\Phi = AH$. Unit = the weber.

Magnetic induction, B.   The magnetic flux induced in a body per unit area at right angles to the direction of the flux.   Unit : the gauss.

Magnetising force (*or magnetic field strength*), *H.*   The magnetic force acting on unit pole.   Unit : the oersted.

Magnetostriction.   The increase in length produced in a magnetic body by a magnetising field.

Paramagnetism/paraelectricity.   The alignment of magnetic/electric dipoles parallel to an applied magnetic/electric field.

Permeability, μ. The ratio of magnetic induction to applied magnetising force. $\mu = B/H$.

Permittivity, dielectric constant, ε (sometimes κ or K). The ratio of the capacitance of a capacitor with the given substance as dielectric, to the capacitance of the same capacitor having air (or strictly vacuum) as the dielectric. For a capacitor in disc form

$$\varepsilon = 144Ct/d^2$$

where C is the capacitance in pF, t the distance between the plates in mm., and d the diameter of the plates in mm. For a tubular capacitor

$$\varepsilon = \frac{41.5C}{L} \log \frac{10a}{b}$$

where C is the capacitance in pF, a and b are the mean outside and inside diameters in mm., and L the length in mm.

Phase angle, ø. The angle by which the current vector leads (capacitor) or lags (inductor) the potential vector.

Phase defect. See power factor.

Piezoelectric coefficient. The electric polarisation in electrostatic units produced per unit mechanical pressure in dynes per cm.². It is also expressed as the ratio of charge to applied force, e.g. in coulombs per newton.

Piezoelectric effect. When certain crystals are subjected to an electric field they expand along one axis and contract along another, depending on the direction of the field. The term *inverse piezo-electric effect* refers to the appearance of electric charges when the crystals are mechanically stressed, the effect again being directional.

Power factor, phase defect, cos ø, sin δ (≃ tan δ for good insulators). The ratio power, i.e. potential × current **in phase**, to the product of total applied potential and current.

Q(uality) factor. The reciprocal of power factor, i.e. $1/\tan \delta$.

Resistivity, specific resistance, ρ. (*a*) Surface resistivity: the resistance of unit length and unit width. Unit : ohms per square. **(Note** : the dimensions of the square are immaterial). (*b*) Volume or bulk resistivity : the resistance of unit cross section and unit length. Unit : ohm cm.

T_e value. The temperature at which the (volume) resistivity of an insulator falls to 10^{-6} ohm cm.

APPENDIX 2

ELECTRICAL AND MAGNETIC MEASUREMENTS

A2.1 Dielectric strength

Test pieces are made in the form of discs with the central area dished on one or both sides so as to ensure that breakdown shall occur well away from the edges of the disc where there would be uneven electric stress ('edge effects'). The thickness at the centre is normally 2—3 mm., so that a voltage around 50—100 kV is necessary to produce breakdown in a high tension porcelain. The dished areas are electroded, for example with cold silvering paste, and where only one side is dished the whole of the opposite side is also electroded (Fig. A2.1). Great care is necessary, particularly in shaping, to avoid defects in such a thin section piece, and a similar method to that used for production should be used if possible in order to be able to relate test results to actual performance. Tests may also be carried out on suitable pieces of production ware dished by grinding.

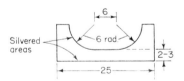

Fig. A2.1.—Dielectric strength test piece. (Dimensions in mm.).

As mentioned earlier, tests are usually done under transformer oil ; the properties of this have a marked influence on the results obtained, and the grade used must be specified. The results are also influenced by temperature, rate of application and duration of the applied voltage, its frequency and wave form, all of which must be standardised.

175

A2.2 Resistivity
Surface resistivity

An approximate value may be obtained by measuring the resistance between two parallel lines of equal length drawn on the surface of a piece of ceramic with graphite or cold silvering paste, but for more accurate values a standard test piece is required. This is in the form of a plain disc, electroded on one side up to 1 mm. or so of the edge. A central circle, roughly half the eara, is electroded on the other side and is surrounded by an electroded annular area between this and the edge. Fig. A2.2 shows a section through the

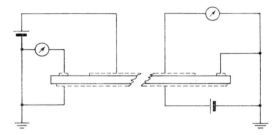

Fig. A2.2.—Resistivity test piece. Left-hand circuit for surface resistivity ; right-hand circuit for volume resistivity.

disc and the electrical connections for measuring the current flowing under a given applied voltage, from which the resistance can be calculated ; knowing the dimensions of the space between the annular electrode and the central electrode on the one side, the resistivity can also be found. It will be seen that only current passing across that area will be registered by the ammeter. Voltages up to 500 V may be applied in the case of high tension porcelain. Since surface resistivity is very dependent on humidity of the atmosphere this must be specified. Precise measurement is very difficult.

Volume resistivity

The same type of test disc is used as for surface resistivity, but the annular electrode is now connected to the opposite face, and the battery, with the ammeter in series, is connected between the latter electrode and the central one. The metallized annular

176

electrode now acts as a guard ring so that any current leaking over the surface by-passes the ammeter. For measurement much above 100°C. it is sometimes possible to dispense with the guard ring. A point to note is that the current tends to fall slightly with time of application of the voltage, eventually reaching a steady value. This is due to polarisation within the specimen, and it is advisable to take a reading after say, 1 minute, then to reverse the polarity, take another reading after 1 minute, and record the mean of the two readings.

As the insulation resistance of ceramics at room temperature is very high the current is obtained in practice by measuring the voltage drop across a standard resistor by means of a sensitive valve voltmeter. Instruments are also available for registering resistances directly up to about 10^{13} ohms or even higher.

A2.3 Permittivity and power factor
(i) At frequencies up to 50 kc/s

The test piece may be in the form of a plain disc, electroded on both faces to form a capacitor. Other shapes may also be used—for example, tubes silvered inside and out. For materials of permittivity less than about 10, tin or aluminium foil electrodes are often used instead of silver, being pressed into close contact with the ceramic (in disc form) ; cylindrical or cup shaped pieces are sometimes tested using mercury electrodes.

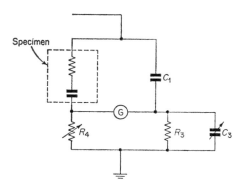

Fig. A2.3.—Principle of Schering bridge. G is a null instrument suitable for a.c., e.g. a vibration galvanometer. Note : specimen is represented as a capacitance and resistance in series.

An A.C. (Schering) bridge is used to obtain both permittivity and power factor. The principle is shown in Fig. A2.3. For use at frequencies above a few hundred c/s special earthing arrangements have to be used in order to avoid errors due to inter-capacitance between the high and low voltage arms of the bridge, and other stray capacitances. Above about 50 kc/s these errors become too large for the bridge to be used. Either low or high voltages can be applied when making measurements. It can be shown that the capacitance of the specimen is equal to R_3C_1/R_4, and the power factor is equal to $2\pi f R_3 C_3$. Knowing the dimensions of the specimen the permittivity can be calculated (see Appendix 1).

(ii) From 20 kc/s to 100 Mc/s

A resonance method is used for this range, the principle of which is illustrated in Fig. A2.4. The frequency of the oscillator is adjusted to the required frequency and the measuring circuit to which it is coupled is tuned to resonance (indicated by a maximum reading on the voltmeter) for that particular frequency, by means

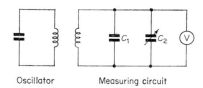

Oscillator　　　　Measuring circuit

Fig. A2.4.—Principle of resonance circuit for measuring permittivity and power factor. C_1—test capacitor ; C_2—measuring capacitor.

of a precision air capacitor. The capacitance, and hence the permittivity of the specimen (usually in disc form) can be determined simply by direct substitution, from the difference between the tuning capacitance necessary to give resonance without the specimen in circuit and when it is connected in parallel with the measuring capacitor. By measuring corresponding the voltages the power factor can be calculated approximately from the relation :—

$$\tan\delta = \frac{(V_1-V_2)\ C_1}{V_1 V_2\ (C_1-C_2)}$$

where V_1, V_2 are the voltages without and with the test capacitor in circuit, and C_1, C_2 the corresponding tuning capacitances.

For very high capacitances, beyond the range of the measuring condenser, such as those obtained with high-permittivity ceramics, the specimen is connected in series instead of in parallel, with corresponding modification of the calculations.

A more accurate method of determining power factor is that due to Hartshorn and Ward, which is incorporated in BS 2067: 1953—"Determination of power factor and permittivity of insulating materials". This consists of measuring the width of the resonance curve at a certain height. It will be seen (Fig. A2.5) that, when the circuit is

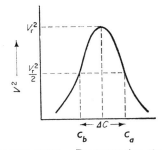

A2.5.—Typical resonance curve.   By measuring the band width, ΔC, at say $\dfrac{V^2_r}{2}$, with and without the test capacitor in circuit, permittivity and tan δ can be calculated.

detuned so that the square of the voltage developed (V^2) is reduced to half its resonance value, the width of the curve is $C_a - C_b = \Delta C$. If the detuning is performed with the specimen in, and again with it out, the widths will be different : the higher the power factor of the specimen the greater the width, i.e. the flatter the tuning, which, of course, is the reason for aiming at low power factors in dielectrics used in radio communications.   The value of the power factor is calculated from the relation :

$$\tan \delta = (\Delta C_i - \Delta C_o) / (2C_s \sqrt{(V^2 - 1)})$$

where ΔC_i and ΔC_o are the widths of the curve with and without the specimen, and C_s is the capacitance of the specimen.

179

The high quality equipment required for the greatest accuracy may cost in the region of £1000 or more, but for routine measurement where a somewhat lower accuracy is acceptable, a Voltage Magnification Meter ('Q-meter'), costing only about a quarter of this, is satisfactory, and in fact is a very useful piece of laboratory equipment for making both dielectric and magnetic measurements.

(iii) For frequencies above 100 Mc/s

At frequencies above about 10 Mc/s the effect of the resistance of the electrodes may introduce errors by making the power factor appear too high, when using a resonance method ; also the inter-electrode distances in valves soon becomes comparable to the wavelength of the oscillations used, giving spurious results. Although it is possible to make measurements somewhat above this frequency quite different methods have to be used at frequencies above about 100 Mc/s. These are based on the setting up of stationary waves in a transmission line containing the dielectric under test. The wavelength, attenuation and other circuit constants can then be obtained, and the permittivity and power factor calculated.

A2.4 Magnetic properties

A Q-meter may be used for making measurements on inductors as well as on capacitors, and therefore inductors containing different core materials may be compared. However, permeability and loss measurements can only be comparative unless ring-shaped specimens (toroids) are used, to provide a closed magnetic circuit; other shapes involve air gaps and only allow the characteristics of the whole assembly to be determined.

For making the various other magnetic measurements very specialised equipment is mostly required, and further discussion of this topic would be out of place here.

REFERENCE

W. P. Baker, "Electrical Insulation Measurement". Geo. Newnes, London, 1965.

APPENDIX 3

TABLE A3.1

Properties of some high temperature ceramics

Property	Units	BeO	MgO	Al$_2$O$_3$ (100%)	SiO$_2$ (fused)	ZrO$_2$ (stabilised)	ThO$_2$	UO$_2$	Graphite (average)	TiB$_2$	ZrB$_2$	CrB$_2$	B$_4$C	SiC	TiC	ZrC	WC	UC	MoSi$_2$	BN	AlN	Si$_3$N$_4$
		←——— OXIDES ———→							←—————————————————————— NON-OXIDES ——————————————————————→										←Silicide→	←—— Nitrides ——→		
										←—Borides—→			←——————— Carbides ———————→									
Theoretical density	g/cc	3.02	3.65	4.0	2.3	5.49	9.69	10.1	2.2	4.52	6.09	5.60	2.52	3.22	4.9	6.7	15.7	13.6	6.3	2.25	3.26	3.18
Melting point	°C.	2575	2800	2050	1710	2700	3050	2176	sublimes	2980	3040	1850—2280	2425	d2300	3250	3175	2620	2550	2050	3000	(2450)	sublimes 1900
Coefficient of linear thermal expansion (20—1000°C.)	°C.$^{-1}$ (×10^{-6})	8.8	13.8	7	0.55	8.8	9.3	9	5 (average) (0°C.)				4.5	4.5	4		5.4	10.9	7.9	{7.5 0.83}	5.5	2.9
Thermal conductivity (at 25°C.)	BTU hr^{-1} ft^{-1}°F.$^{-1}$	130	26	70	0.57	1.0	6.0	7	25—350	35			19	1500	20	25	20	16	32	{11 18}	20	5
Modulus of rupture (bending strength)	lb. in^{-2} (×10^3)	37	15	60	5	26	26	26	1—16	19	45	75—100	50	30	32	50	50	15	55	13	38	90
Modulus of elasticity (Young's modulus)	lb. in^{-2} (×10^6)	50	45	55	10	23	35	28		70	60	31	65	50	50	58	100		59	15	50	40

NOTE—

Many of the above figures (apart from theoretical densities) are typical values for high quality products and are necessarily imprecise owing to variations in composition, manufacturing methods, bulk density and conditions of measurement, and should therefore only be used for purposes of comparison.

181

APPENDIX 4

TABLE A4.1

Properties of high frequency, high permittivity and magnetic ceramics

Property	Units	Low Loss Steatite	Zircon Porcelain	95% Alumina	Rutile	Magnesium Titanate	Calcium Titanate	Strontium Titanate	Barium Titanate (Capacitor)	Barium Titanate (Piezo-electrics)	Lead Zirconate Titanate	Manganese Zinc Ferrite	Nickel Zinc Ferrite	Manganese Magnesium Ferrite	Barium Ferrite
Bulk density	g/cc.	2.7	3.6	3.7	3.7	3.3	~4	~5	5.2	5.3	~8	4.8	4.4		4.8
Permittivity	—	6	5	9.0	100	14	140	240	4000	1200	1500	10^5	100		
Temperature Coefficient of Permittivity	$°C^{-1}$ $\times 10^{-6}$	+140			−750	+100	−1500	−2400	variable	variable					
Tan δ (at 1 Mc/s)	$\times 10^{-4}$	6	12	3	3	1	5	5	150	200 at 10 kc/s		400 (at 250 kc/s)		250	
Resistivity	ohm—cm	10^{13}	10^{14}	10^{14}	10^{13}	10^{13}	10^{12}	10^{12}	10^{13}	10^{10}	10^{10}	130	10		10^8
T_c	°C.	900	800	850	500										
Permeability (initial)	—	—	—	—	—	—	—	—	—	—	—	1000	500	40	
Remanence	gauss											300		1600	2700
Coercive force	oersted											0.4	0.4	1.5	2000

182

TECHNICAL CERAMICS

INDEX

INDEX

C

INDEX

DATE DUE

NOV 25			
NOV 23			
SEP 21			
OCT 15			
DEC 07			
MAR 25			